Ann –

Your enthusiastic support from the early days through a close-to-final version was critical to my staying power. I very much appreciate and respect your opinion and words.

Linda 11/20/09

Yes, I Can!

a journal of my journey from
senior citizen to senior athlete

by Linda Scifers Glick

GLAM Communications, LLC
Colorado Springs, Colorado

Yes, I Can

a journal of my journey from senior citizen to senior athlete

ISBN 13-978-0-615-32515-6

Cover design and layout by Lorayne McGovern

Cover photo courtesy of Rocky Mountain Senior Games

This journal is dedicated,
with appreciation and love,
to Mary Ann Kluge
my colleague, coach, trainer
and friend extraordinaire.
Thanks for changing my life.

Special Thanks to

My kids and grandkids for believing in me and sending me the cool clothes: Tom, Maria, Charlie, Teddy, Maisy, James, Rachel, Samantha and John Glick and Christa Ambrose

Mary Ann Kluge for being my coach and trainer

Ann Stratten for early and continued encouragement

The Bookies: Mary Ann Kluge, Linda Kohlman, Vicki Levine, Ellen Levy, and Laurie Picus for listening, supporting, and believing

Pat Vert-Beville for such good body care

Sue Dilloway for last minute proofing

Lorayne McGovern for making this look good

Manuela da Ponte for such friendly printing advice

Healing Thoughts to

My sister-in-law Marilyn Prince

One of the Gs, Karen Cloud Burnidge

Introduction

I have an interest in changing perceptions about older people. Rather than allowing appearance or life-experience-to-date to dictate worth, I believe that if we dig deeper, at any time in our lives, there is vast potential in all of us. Life's transitions provide opportunities to discover aspects of ourselves we never knew we had. This journal-memoir invites readers to see how one equally "ordinary" and "extraordinary" woman ventured out into uncharted territory later in life. Her experience has been life-changing for her and for many others who have heard her story.

I have, in my career, coached and trained people of all ages and ability levels: working with Linda was unique. The experience for me as her coach and trainer was both challenging and rewarding, the rewards being more than I ever could have predicted in terms of positive outcomes for Linda, for me, and for those who know of this venture. I and many others respect her bravery and courage (and those are the words people use) and share her sense of joy and pride.

While this is Linda's story – her journal entries, poetry, and reflections during a seven-month slice of her life – at the heart of this story is so much more. The discoveries and connections Linda made for herself and others serve as an example of what can happen if you step up to the starting line at anytime in your life and believe, as Linda did, that "yes, you can!"

Common themes for women (and some men) of all ages make this book accessible to all. Linda's writing style is honest, revealing, entertaining, and thought provoking. This story will capture your heart and inspire you to believe that it is never too late to dare to do something new and exciting.

Enjoy!

Mary Ann Kluge, PhD
Linda's Trainer and Coach
Associate Professor, Health Sciences
Beth-El College of Nursing and Health Sciences
University of Colorado at Colorado Springs

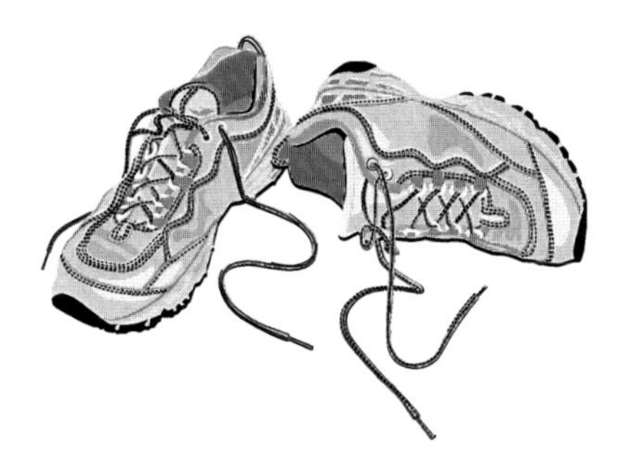

THE STARTING LINE

During the summer of 2005, with absolutely no effort on my part, I gained 10 pounds between my waist and my knees. I knew I had to do something. Then on November first I got my Medicare card. A sobering event. And I thought getting my AARP card was depressing. I am getting desperate.

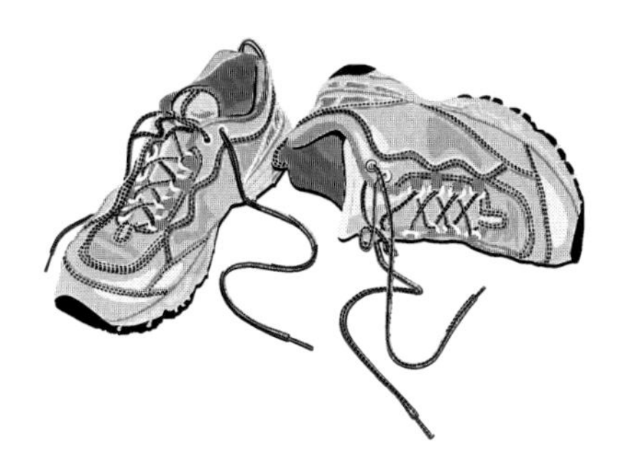

NOVEMBER 2005

November 2

Bevan, a professor from a university in New Zealand, was visiting my friend and teaching colleague, Mary Ann. Bevan and his wife, Lorraine, teach and have expertise in older adult fitness. Lorraine focuses on ethnography, whatever that means. Bevan brought a DVD, *Racing Against the Clock.*

As I watched that DVD, I kept thinking, "I could do that." There were all of these old women (each I'm sure with her own Medicare card) running, jumping, leaping, and actually competing in something called The Senior Olympics. They had saggy arms and fat splotchy legs and wrinkly faces and gray hair; I could do that.

So when Mary Ann asked me what I thought of the video, that's what I said. "I could do that."

"Do you want to?" she asked. "Because if you do, I'll help you. You could compete in the Rocky Mountain Senior Games, and I would be your trainer."

I said yes.

November 5

The Bookies, as my husband refers to my women's book club, went to the Rocky Mountain Women's Film Festival. At the Film Makers' Forum someone asked if these women film makers would advise their daughters to be film makers. The answer was, "Everyone can be a film maker. Everyone has a story to tell. Get a camera." Sitting next to Mary Ann, I noted that she began to scribble a To Do List:

Buy a camera
Get film makers' insurance, etc.

That evening, when Mary Ann and her husband Ken joined us for dinner, Mary Ann announced a plan to do an ethnography as part of my training for The Senior Games. After I agreed, I made a mental note to look up that word.

I also got on the internet and read about Senior Games. Virtually every state has Senior Games for people 50 years and older. Individuals compete in age groups (50-54, 55-60, etc.) There are more than 20 events from Track and

Field to Table Tennis.

That same evening at dinner was when we decided together that I will train for the 100 meter sprint. Mary Ann pointed out that I need an event that is short and fast and in a straight line to align with my directional challenges and rabbit personality. Short and straight should lessen the chances that I will get lost as I can easily do in someone's home and certainly on highways and no, I can't just "reverse the directions" to return. But I digress. The rabbit thing is about my not being a long distance anything except for relationships and feelings.

Mary Ann and me at an event.

Those I do for long times; but I work and play in spurts. I like to change tasks and topics quickly. I get bored and/or tired easily. My focus is intense and my energy explodes. Then I need to rest or change the pace. So, a short race. But a long jump? I don't know where that came from. I have never done a long jump. I simply said I'd like to try that too.

It was about here that Mary Ann said that we both would need to keep journals. She will make me a getting-into-shape plan. I already have a few exercises that she has outlined for me. I am to continue those but not much else and no running. We must build to that, she says. Okay. I like to jump into projects. Duh, maybe that's where the long jump thing came from. Freud pops up everywhere whether you believe in him or not. At that point I gave control to Mary Ann. With a PhD in Gerontology with an emphasis on fitness, she has expertise in this area. I trust her judgment and plans.

Then we began to talk about clothes for running. The clothes are cool. One of the women in that *Racing Against the Clock* video had these killer tights that I absolutely must find. Mary Ann said that running shoes might cost $100.

Sunday, November 6

I woke up thinking about buying that camera. I looked at ads and at 8:20 called My Trainer. That is so cool. I have never had a trainer before for anything. She is ordering a book about ethnography. I am beginning to understand that an ethnography is about telling one's tale. I went shopping for a camera.

I feel good just thinking about all of this. What a kick it would be to get into shape and to be in competitions. I was born in 1940 and graduated from college in 1962. I was absolutely oblivious to any women's sports. When I was growing up in Pittsburg,– no "H" – Kansas, I never heard of little league for girls. The only "sports" I participated in were in P.E. class. The most notable one was basketball where three girls were forwards and played on one side of the court and three girls were guards and played on the other side of the court. Stepping on the line was a violation. Did a man make those rules?

That slightly feminist voice of mine did not find sound until, oh I'd say, the 80's. When I think back about how unenlightened and downright woman-wimpy I was.....

For instance, after my high-school sweetheart, Keith, whom I married, was in the Army in Killeen, Texas from 1963-1965, we moved to the Boston area. Talk about culture shock, a term I was not then familiar with but an experience I began living. After my first five minutes of driving in Harvard Square, I just pulled over and cried for awhile. I adjusted, perhaps too well. My sister-in-law, Marilyn, still relates how, when she visited us in Needham, I turned the wrong way onto a one-way street in downtown Boston, explaining that it was the only way I knew how to get to where I wanted to be. I got so I could wheedle and nudge and almost but not quite scrape that car trying to get into my lane with the best of them. So far, in my experience, only Rome and Cairo have more challenging traffic than Boston.

I got a last minute, week-before-school-started job in a suburban school district that was being touted (on the cover of TIME) as one of the best in the nation. It must have been about then that Harvard began turning out Master's in Teaching graduates, and they were in male abundance at my new high school. I liked my classes, although hearing students say "fuck you" in the hallways was a bit of a jolt to me growing up in Pittsburg Kansas and then teaching for two years in Killeen/Fort Hood, Texas, where students almost saluted teachers. Everyone else in the social studies department in my new school was male and a Harvard graduate. In the teachers' lounge (where people still smoked!) I heard the midwest referred to as "those big square states" and learned that East coast people went to New York, California, Florida and Europe, but never ever to Kansas. I taught in that Newton high school for almost two years before I realized that the Social Studies Department had regular meetings. I was not invited/included. Pretty simple: I was not male or Harvard, and worst of all perhaps, I was from a big square state. At the time I didn't even feel insulted. Nor did I confront anyone about not being included. That's what I mean about woman-wimpy. I am now clear that women are, at the least, equal to men and should be treated as such. One of my stamps says it best, "Remember, Ginger Rogers did everything Fred Astaire did, but she did it backwards and in high heels." (Faith Whittlesey)

Back to the fact that competing in sports was not in my decade's vocabulary. My gym class was kind of like a boot camp with exercises and an in-your-face gym teacher with a loud whistle. Girls couldn't do too much. Certainly you couldn't swim when you had your period. We didn't actually say the word, "period." When we had our menstrual cycle, and P.E. roll was called, we'd say, "Observing." That meant you had your period so you couldn't run or jump or swim and certainly never ride a horse. Although mysteriously unstated, the message we received was that when you were "observing," doing things like riding horses or swimming would affect your "womanhood" – your ability to have children. We used Kotex pads. Oh, did we use Kotex pads. It was an expensive process in terms of toilet paper usage. The used pad was first folded and wrapped several times one way in tissue and then around the other way and then back again several times until the package finally put into the waste basket was almost the size of a bread box.

I am remembering those days. I can see the locker room. 1956. It seems that a part of me from then is doing this new adventure. I have not previously felt a loss about no girlhood sports in my growing up years. It is more that I am newly aware that there has been an empty space in my life. I did not even know it was there, and I'm now filling that space. It's not as though I have actively missed such opportunities. If you don't know about something, you can't really miss it. You can miss out, I guess, but not miss it. The whole idea of competing and (I sort of whisper what seems an unlikely thought) being an athlete is totally new. It's kind of like when a friend, after reading some of my poetry, nudged me into saying, "I am a poet." I am nudging me to say, "I am going to be an athlete." I like it.

Breathing

I haven't mentioned breathing. I have two breathing exercises. The one nostril at a time one where I close the left nostril by gently pressing my finger on it and then inhale into the right; then hold that right nostril shut and exhale out of the left nostril. And the Yogi breath which I think means I am to inhale deeply, taking the air first into my abdomen and then lungs, and finally out the top of my head; and then pant/puff to get more/all of the air out. Mary Ann explains why I'm to do these. I can't remember. She says not to do too much these first few weeks. Thank goodness.

I walked one mile today. And every once in awhile I tried to do the power walking M.A. mentioned where I walk as fast as I can while counting aloud (that way I know if I can breathe) to 20. Then I walk regular speed until I "recover" which means I can breathe well; then I walk fast and count to 30; recover until I can breathe well; then walk fast and count to 40. Repeat the 30 and the 20. The counting goes well, but the walking fast is weird. I think I look like a mannequin that is trying to escape. The breathing is okay and I feel good that I have done this much. I tried to do the Downward Dog when I got home but couldn't remember how. So I ate the rest of the butter pecan ice cream with hot fudge sauce on it and then had potato chips and some shaved ham. All in all, a good first session on my own, I think.

M.A. has designed some exercises for balance, some for agility, and some for strength. I don't know all the muscle and ligament vocabulary; but the concept makes sense to me. The Stork is about standing on one foot, raising the other foot, and staying balanced. I can do a quick count to four before I tip to one side. Mary Ann told me about propioceptors. I love how that word feels coming out of my mouth.

I love words; in college I wanted to major in English and then write the great American novel. My mother pointed out that I might need a real job with a regular salary. Back then, in the early sixties, the predominant thinking (at least in my family and town) was that women could/should be teachers or nurses or secretaries. I did get a teaching degree and taught high school English and Social Studies and realized that I love to teach. Actually, I love to perform. Perhaps I will be an actress in my next life? I'm good in the classroom and am proud of my 2003 Outstanding Instructor Award from the

University of Colorado in Colorado Springs.

With my love for words I am appalled at what is happening to our language. Young people seem only to hear the language rather than read it. They quickly scan whatever blog or internet site they click to. They text-message using abbreviations I don't comprehend. But do they read books and learn vocabulary? When I get my university students' papers I keep a list of "words" my students use. One student talked about the different "rolls" her family members have; another young woman was "up hauled" at her boyfriend's inattention. Spell check won't take care of those mistakes.

I wonder if kids read books any more. When I had a conference with one of my students, a college senior, she told me how much she enjoyed *Tuesdays with Morrie*, a required book for my Death and Dying class. She added that this was the first book she had ever read "all the way through." She was graduating from college.

Back to propioceptors. As I understand it, these propioceptors are hooked up from my feet to my spinal cord and when I slip and am about to fall, the spinal cord sends a message to my body/feet to catch myself. But that reception line needs to be kept clear and open or the messages won't get through and I may fall. The way to have a direct and open line for the messages is to keep exercising my feet and doing my balance exercises which take a maximum of three minutes. Not a bad investment for not falling. I knew that a common cause of injury for older adults is falling, often with a broken hip as a result. I looked on the Center for Disease Control website. The statistics I found there are worse than I thought. I will add them to my after-notes. I am convinced to work on my balance.

Another "exercise" that I like is The Alphabet. Anytime, like when I'm watching TV, I put my legs out straight and up on a foot stool or table and then "write" the alphabet with my toes – not my legs. I can tell where my feet are tight. Windshield Wipers is another one. That is when I have my feet flat on the floor and then, keeping my heels on the floor I lift my toes up and move my feet back and forth like windshield wipers. Such a simple and easy and almost anywhere (on an airplane, at a lecture, in a car) good thing to do for feet, ankles and propioceptors.

Later that evening I tried to do my StepUps where I step onto this little blue, plastic, kitchen step stool with one foot, then put that foot down on the floor, then put the other foot up on the stool, and so on. I finally get the rhythm.

I like these. I don't quite have the hand thing yet when I'm supposed to have the left arm punching forward when my right foot is on the stool and the right arm punching when my left foot is on the stool. I'll get it.

I have told several people what I am doing. Announcing to others is a way I commit.

hoe

Today was Shoe Day. I have flat feet that turn in, and they seem to get sore and tired easily. My trainer wants us to pay particular attention to my feet. We were at the Runner's Roost for 1½ hours! I would go outside the shop and run up and down the sidewalk while The Shoe Guy watched me. I have these bones on the top of my feet which protrude. They didn't used to do that. Many things on my body have changed! Most shoes hurt when they go across those bones. The Shoe Guy was brilliant. He simply laced the shoes so the laces do not go across those bones. So simple really. After trying on and jogging in about six pair of shoes, I, with the consent of my trainer and The Shoe Guy, chose some that cost $110! I didn't even pay that much for shoes for my kids' weddings. I am disappointed that the shoes do not have those spike things in the bottom and are not very jazzy looking; but I guess I accept that fit is more important for running.

on training for the senior games - a shoe-in?

Imelda Marcos I'm not
but I do like shoes

hard then to swallow
buying shoes
expensive shoes
because they fit

no consideration of color
no delving into design

one hundred and how many dollars?
I should have those babies bronzed

don't say bronze
only gold

run me to the gold
you gorgeous
foot fitting into
most perfect
shoes

Tights and Thumb-holes

Then I tried on clothes. Those tights I saw in the *Racing Against the Clock* video are to die for, and they have built in knee braces and thigh stabilizers, so the tag says. Then there are these shirts with thumb holes in the bottom of the sleeves. I love those thumb hole things! Mary Ann says that I will probably need Training Colors and Competition Colors. So right.

I didn't buy anything yet.

Friday, November 11

Mary Ann and I went to a track, actually to two high school tracks. They were both fenced off and had No Trespassing signs. I suppose they are locked because of vandalism. I would note, however, that I pay taxes for these schools and I want to be able to use the facilities. I will deal with that later. For today, we sucked in our tummies and got through a gap in the fence. It was the first time I had been on a track with the thought of using it. The track was all marked with lines and lanes and numbers and arrows and looked quite official. I wasn't expecting to feel excited, kind of like a 16 year old. I guess I mean that the feelings I had are young feelings, like this new adventure is truly possible. For the first time in my life, I felt like an athlete. I was exhilarated.

M.A. became very trainer-like and measured my stride and had me walk "regular" and then walk "as fast as I can." She counted my steps. We also did some heart rate things. I got the general idea and was glad she was doing the math.

We walked all around the track and saw the sand pits for jumping. I really want to try that. I do not, however, like to be jostled. I hope I like the jumping, and most of all hope I don't bang my head. My trainer says that I am not ready to jump yet. Sometimes I watch myself in amazement as I accept the do's and do not's Mary Ann tells me. I am a fairly independent woman, but all of this training and athletic information is new to me. I am a smart enough woman to take advice from an expert whom I trust. So "to infinity and beyond."

After counting steps some more I asked if it would be okay to try running the 100 meter. M.A. timed me. What I realized as I was running was that I have forgotten how to run. I can jog although I have never done that as exercise. As I was running I was aware that my legs didn't seem to know how to stride out in front the way my mind thought they should. I probably have not even tried to run fast for more than 50 years. No wonder my body has forgotten how.

24 seconds. I don't know what that means except I know I can and will do better.

M.A. gave me my first exercise sheets. I like them.

I am fantasizing about medals. I like to win. I like to be recognized. I like all of this.

And I want those black and silver tights.

November 12, A Saturday

Mary Ann gave me four Yoga poses to do: Downward Dog, Bridge, a stretch and something else. We went over my Getting Into Shape Plan for the first few weeks. I don't want to disappoint her; but there seems to be so much and so many things to do. And I'm tired. I taught for almost four hours this afternoon. I fell asleep during Monday Night Football. Sound asleep. I went to bed before the game was over. And I'm sore. Not sore awful but definitely sore. My upper legs mainly. And my back a little. Am I a wimp? Am I going to be 65 in two weeks?

M.A. told me that the woman who won the 100 meter in my age group in Colorado a couple of years ago ran it in 22+ seconds. Well, I ran it in 24 for the first time even with my knees not "leading" so I can do under 22. I do want to win. June is a long way off. And I'm already tired.

November 15

M.A. and I had a presentation at a women's conference in Denver. Afterwards we stopped at a Reebok outlet. They had those shirts with thumb-holes. You put your thumb through this little loop on the sleeve. Then your sleeves stay down. I think it will help with warmth but mainly I just like them. I want one of those shirts. We are gathering information and pricing things. I was all shopped out, having done Nordstrom's for two plus hours. Got some dynamite black boots that are narrow and actually fit.

I forget how to do some of the exercises. I know it's important to have hands and other body parts in the right place: "wrists in line with elbows," and "knees over ankles" so you can see your toes.

I feel a bit dim not remembering what The Windmill is and how to do the Downward Dog. I do remember The Bridge. I like choosing and having names that make sense to me for all of my exercises… if I can remember them! And I like doing them in spurts, like during a commercial of "Commander in Chief."

I need to start some new things tomorrow. It's when I walk, then walk fast for 20 seconds, etc. I think we're calling them Intervals… or something like that. I'm going to bed now. Except I will do two more stretch things first.

I am even writing like a junior high school kid. Middle Schools didn't exist in the 50s in my small Kansas town.

November 18

I did my first (by myself) "interval" walking. I did a 1/2 mile warm-up and then did 40 fast steps, counting out loud. Full recovery, then 50 fast; recovery; 40 fast again. I did not get out of breath.

November 20

I did what has become my routine: Ice Cream Cones for ankles, Knee Circles, Hula Hoops for hips, then two yoga stretches, my shoulder things, StepUps on the blue plastic stool, and lunges. I can add a few more reps of each now. I smile as I type "reps." I'm even learning some of the jargon.

An Idea

I got this idea about having all the Gs do the Senior Games together. When I asked Mary Ann what she thought about that, she loved the idea.

When I was in junior high school in Pittsburg, Kansas, we had a "gang" which had nothing to do with GANGS. Were there any then? If so, I sure didn't know about them. We called ourselves the Giggling, Gossiping, Girls and even had cuff links with Gs engraved on them. One G on each cuff link and the third G was for the Girl wearing the cuff links! We had such fun. We had slumber parties, went to movies, went steady with the same boys (at different times), went to Rainbow and DeMolay formals, and were true pals. We went roller skating every Friday night. Sometimes there were eleven or thirteen of us piled in one car with one parent driving. We wore our jeans rolled up and our Dads' white shirts. Quite the fashionable group in the mid-1950s. We also went to the swimming pool at the park quite a bit, although I less than the others for a couple of reasons: 1) I couldn't swim; and 2) at age 12 I started working at my Aunt Susie's and Uncle Charlie's ice cream plant, the **P**ittsburg **I**ce **C**ream **CO**mpany. Everyone went to the **PICCO** to get nickel or dime (two scoops) cones, six or eleven cent cherry limeades, twenty cent milk shakes (five cents more with malt) and 35 cent banana splits. I made 35 cents an hour. I worked there every summer, even through college, and by then I made $1.00 an hour.

I couldn't swim because when my brother Terry and I were seven and three years old, we were diagnosed with asthma. Our folks took us to Oklahoma City to a specialist there. That was probably quite expensive. We had to take little red pills and get shots at home and we were never to put our heads under water. At least that's what our mother heard the doctor say and gave us as a mantra. This was such a command in my head that to this day I have trouble having my head under the shower. I do not like water in my face. Neither Terry nor I learned to swim. Well, that's not exactly true. I took swimming lessons after my children were born. I thought it was a responsible thing for a mother to do. So, I can, technically, swim. I can do the arms and legs; I just can't put my face in the water or take breaths. When water gets in my face, my arms and legs forget what to do. Total panic. Thus, my swimming is limited in duration and distance. I used to get mildly panicked at being on a boat. I am mostly over that now although I feel much better wearing a life vest, even on a short boat ride.

As for asthma, I don't think we had it. I think we had allergies. Our grandparents had feather beds; we had fluffy cats (I am, as an adult, allergic to cats); and we lived in Kansas, the Mecca of hay fever.

Back to The Gs

In, and especially after, high school, we sort of drifted apart. There wasn't a break-up of any kind, just drifting. Veet and Saragene kept in touch. Judy and I kept in touch. Sporadic Christmas cards. Once when we were 40 or so, we all met at Jim's steak house on a summer evening when someone realized we were all in town. That was a fun time. And then more drifting. Different states. Husbands. Children. Jobs.

In 1998 we went to our 40th High School reunion. The organizer asked our gang/The Gs to sing a song. I made up some silly thing and we went to Saragene's house to rehearse it. We had a blast. We laughed so hard we hurt. Just like we used to. What an incredible instant bonding, or, I guess, re-bonding. We had such a terrific time that we said we should get together again soon. In early 1999, Veet and I met in Kansas City (she lived near there and my brother Terry lived there), and over lunch decided to try for a get-together. Veet has a lovely second home on The Lake of the Ozarks and offered that as the meeting place. We decided on a short weekend, chose dates, and sent out invitations to the Gs that came most prominently to our minds. That was the summer of 2000. Everyone we invited came except Saragene. Her husband,

Warren, was potentate of the Shrine that year and she had a must-attend function with him. She hasn't missed one G Gathering since.

At Veet's lake house, we got caught up on the previous 40 years, sharing intimate details of our tragedies and triumphs, including one divorce, one widow-hood, and multiple children. We drank. We smoked. (None of us smokes in our current lives!!!) We laughed. We stayed up until one or two in the morning. It was as if we had just been away from each other a short period of time and picked up the conversation and ran with it. We talked about that, about how comfortable we felt. We talked a lot about our parents, the values they instilled in us, the small town we grew up in, and how our selves still connected. Wow.

In 2001 we went to the Lake House again. Judy drove from Indiana; Karen from Oklahoma; Saragene and Joanie from Kansas; Veet from Missouri; and I flew from Colorado. When we went out to dinner at an Italian restaurant the last night at the lake, we started talking about where and when to meet again. Saragene said, "Well, I've always wanted to go to Italy." We all locked eyes, grinned wildly, raised our wine glasses, and said "To Italy." In the summer of 2002 we had a trip of a lifetime with three days in Rome and a week in a villa in Tuscany. None of us is sure which was the best: planning and anticipating and telling absolutely everyone about it; doing it; or remembering and replaying it.

I kept notes all through Italy and typed them up for each of The Gs.

As I wrote that sentence, I just had to go back and re-read those notes and add a few excerpts to my memory bank here, in this journal.

Five Women. No Men? The Gs In Italy!!! May 2002

A toast to the Gs: Karen, Judy, Saragene, Veet and me.

We began our adventure with on time flights. The five of us met in Chicago and headed to a bar to gear up for the flight to Rome. That flight over the ocean was uneventful except for Karen losing her bottle of Scotch. Saragene went up and down the aisle asking, "Anyone seen a bottle of Scotch rolling in the aisle?" Judy, Veet, and I tried to look like we were travelling separately from those crazy American women.

Customs was a non-event in Rome, and there was a man with a GGG sign. He said not a word and got his 60 Euros as we piled out at The Hotel Modigliani, a charming 24 room hotel on via Puraficazione, which is adjacent to Via Veneto and near Piazza Barberini. We left our bags and headed out to The Spanish Steps. Saragene pointed out that "Spanish" in Italian is "Espagne" which rhymes with lasagna. Useful. We began what would become hours of window shopping with initial observations which eventually became conclusions that Italian fashions are way cool and way expensive; that Italian men of all ages are always helpful and usually flirtatious; and that young Italian women don't seem to care if we are lost in direction or language.

The Forum and the sunset seemed to be waiting for us. We slowly trod where Julius Caesar and Cleopatra (the real one and the Liz one) had gone before us. The sense of history was almost palpable; and the weather and light were perfect. We then found a pizzeria across from the Coliseum and watched the sun set with gorgeous blue and orange colors streaming through the "windows" of that huge round structure. Rodrigo was our waiter. He said he is a friend of the guy from It's A Beautiful Life *– the one who jumped over the chairs at the Oscars. We chose to believe him as he was just as effusive and funny and charming. He treated us like movie stars and began the line we were to have echoed with most of our waiters, "Five Women: No Men?" We were in love with Rome.*

after three days in Rome...

On Saturday we went to Hertz in downtown Rome to get our seven passenger minivan. Judy had volunteered to drive. We piled in; Judy started the van; and the van jumped. Again.

And again.

And again.

At that point I ventured, "Do you have the clutch in?"

"Clutch? What clutch?"

Judy had never learned to drive a standard shift car.

Being a determined woman, Judy said that she could learn how to use a clutch and shift so we, as Saragene so aptly described it, hopped into Rome traffic with Judy at the wheel. We began our close to suicidal vehicular adventure by getting lost and hopping a lot and stopping to re-start the van and then hopping some more. Only one moped driver gave us the finger; we, being generous, gave him four in return. Judy kept both hands on the wheel and did not run over him.

What an adventure that was! Did we have fun! The Gs vowed to meet once or twice a year and have done so with road trips to our homes in Kansas, Missouri, Indiana, Oklahoma, and Colorado plus a trip to Florida and several more week-ends at the Lake of the Ozarks house. We have a flower fund, and when anything really big happens, like when Saragene's mother died, or Veet's sister died, or when Judy got re-married, we send flowers or plants or wine. Saragene's mother had collected, displayed, and presented showings of vintage clothes. Each of the Gs have one of her hats from the 30's or 40's and have vowed to come to each other's funeral and wear the hats. Fortunately, we haven't had to test that pledge yet.

It was not surprising then, that I thought that the Senior Games would be a fun thing to do together – us old broads, The Gs. Mary Ann and I discussed it; she suggested a volleyball team.

The Gs in Colorado: me, Karen, Veet. Saragene and Judy.

In November, after I had started my training, I had coffee in Kansas with Saragene and shared the idea of the Gs having a volleyball team and competing in The Senior Games. She practically jumped up and down. Saragene reiterated that we never got to do those things when we were in high school even though our gang was athletic, with cheerleaders, majorettes, and volleyball players (in gym class). She added, "I can't do races because I have little short legs." Then she added, "Oh, we'll all have to have matching uniforms and choose colors!" My sentiments exactly.

As I am writing, my mind is in a groove about friendship. Judith Viorst is a favorite author and poet; her *Necessary Losses* is a reference book for me as I experience different stages of my life. I required that book for my Death and Dying class; it is, I think, brilliant in its presentation of loss as an everyday occurrence in our lives.

At any rate, Viorst talks about Convenience Friends who exchange rides to the airport, borrow the big turkey roaster, and trade other small favors. Rarely do these friends share intimate thoughts.

Viorst labels Special-interest Friends who belong to the same golf club, or work together, or attend a weekly Pilates class. I think of people I teach with. We see each other in the hall, attend meetings together, have celebratory lunches and a holiday party. There may be regular contact but no intimate sharing.

Historical Friends (Viorst again) knew us back when. I think of Veet. We met at age three, went in and out of our houses together, ran to either of our mothers with a bee sting, went all through school together, dated some of the same flat-topped haircut boys, and still keep in touch.

Viorst mentions other kinds of friends and finally lists Close Friends. I hope every woman has at least one close friend. I am lucky to have had several close friends in my life. As I graduated from high school and then college, moved to different parts of the country, and moved into different parts of my life, I have developed close women friends. Mary C. was my high school confidant. I struggled as to whether I should share that her love had a girl in every port. Had I read Ann Landers at that time in my life, that would probably have been her advice. That shared information with my friend put a damper on our friendship; and we lost touch in college. And she married him years later.

College at K.U. was like a whole new planet to me, with several close friends. As I write that and contemplate what "close friends" means, "several" seems unlikely. However, in that space of my life, several close friends was a reality. I wonder if, for many young women who are 18, that age is one of discovery and experimentation; so taking chances seems to fit. Here I am not talking about drugs or sex; remember, that was still the 50s. I'm thinking about vulnerability, taking a risk to bare your soul. I remember so many nights of soul-baring in college; classes seemed superfluous.

In my senior year at KU Lois Ann Ragsdale and I started to become good friends.

Rags and I did our student teaching together in Topeka; taught at the same Kansas City high school; got our first ever apartment; stopped the car one night to listen to President Kennedy talk on the radio about the Cuban Missile Crisis.

We each got married. Rags travelled the world with her Navy husband. We wrote stacks of letters, in which we discussed everything from our latest hairstyle to the passionate moments with our husbands. I named our first son Thomas Allen (Allen being Rags' last name by then). And then Rags died at age 30. There is still a hole in my heart. I kept all of the letters but when I try to read them I miss her too much and cry too much, so I bundle them up and tie the purple ribbon around them and put them back in the box.

Dona and I taught together in the Boston area. We shared the raising of our children, Sunday night taco dinners, caravan trips to Kansas, rentals on Cape Cod each summer with kids and husbands, and every little and big thought and feeling we had for at least 20 years. Then I moved 2000 miles away, and we had some falling apart. The feelings of anger, disappointment, abandonment, etc. seem in direct proportion to the feelings of love and caring in a soul-mate relationship. Dona and I did not speak or write for several years. By then, in our mid-60s, could we even remember what happened? What we both realized is that we did not want to be estranged when one of us dies. So we agreed to let the past be, whatever it was, and connect again to some of the old and comfortable caring we had shared.

I talked with Pat, my massage therapist, about the need for and the wonderment of women's connections. She noted that women who come to her for massage often share intimate details of their lives; and she never sees them or talks with them until the next appointment in two or three weeks. I wonder if those are some of the women who do not have soul mates yet have a profound need to articulate their feelings. I worry in some global way about women who do not have soul mates. What do they do with their wonderings, their disappointments, their failures, their successes, their depression? Sometimes I will hear a woman in a grocery store check-out line go over the edge of appropriate grocery store talk and speak of a deep hurt or a gnawing grief or words that suggest some kind of fear or abuse. All of this is spoken to a complete stranger, in only a moment or two, and left hanging as the groceries are loaded into the cart.

I was in Ireland at a bus stop and not sure it was the right bus stop. A woman walked up and smiled. I asked her if this was the bus to down-town Dublin. She said yes. We exchanged a few pleasantries. Was I American? From what state? Did I like Ireland? Then, with no warning, she began telling me about the problems she was having with menopause and her husband and their sex life. I didn't even know her name. The bus came. We got on. The end.

Why all of these thoughts? And why and how have I been so fortunate? With just a few more thoughts I will leave this analysis; but right now it feels important to get some of this on paper. I think the answer to my question may be naiveté or an over-active trust or unbridled need to have meaningful contact. So, I just jump in and make that contact. I suppose I must give myself credit for sensing when that is safe with a particular person – some sense that that woman would not think me crazy or that I am coming on to her. Looking back, I realize that I have often pushed for more intimacy with my women friends. I cannot imagine how desolate my life would feel without them.

There are so many things in my women's world that I cherish. Sharing intimate thoughts, feelings, out-of-control laughter or tears; noticing and plucking that chin hair; having a bitchy day accepted; admitting jealousy and envy; calling at 1 a.m. in a panic about a teen-age kid not home yet – putting a real me out there and getting a reassuring and accepting hug – those are just a few gifts from my women friends. I have also found soul-mates in Colorado.

Men can be nice and supportive and often necessary; but they're not women.

Whew. Glad to get that out. Now I absolutely must stretch before I go to bed.

People Die in November

My training routine and our lives were interrupted with the death of my husband's mother, Velma Glick. She was a nice person, a smart and generous woman, and a loving grandmother. Her two children, five grandchildren, and five of her six great-grandchildren were able to be at her funeral in Pittsburg, Kansas. Two Gs also came.

Thanksgiving, in Kansas City with our kids and grandkids, followed as did my 65th birthday. I think I did well with my exercise program given all of that. I used the hotel stairs instead of the elevator-six floors. I suppose I should add that I took the stairs down, not up. I got in a few walks, did my StepUps almost every day (I took my little blue plastic stool with me), and did my stretches for my shoulders. Most important, middle son John gave me a white, hooded, very definite exercise outdoorsy shirt with thumb holes. My wardrobe is shaping up. Keith gave me mega bucks of gift certificates for the Spa at The Broadmoor. I had never been to a spa before Mary Ann introduced me to the experience. I absolutely love all of it: the steam room, an aroma room, the shower with eight shower heads, the Jacuzzi, and the treatments. Oh. The treatments. A scrub, a hot stone massage. This is a whole world of pleasure that I knew nothing about.

It is also noteworthy that I ate sensibly except for the pralines and fudge which I made and which are excellent. Our doctor son John said that the average American gains nine pounds over the Thanksgiving and December holidays. Who needs to know that?

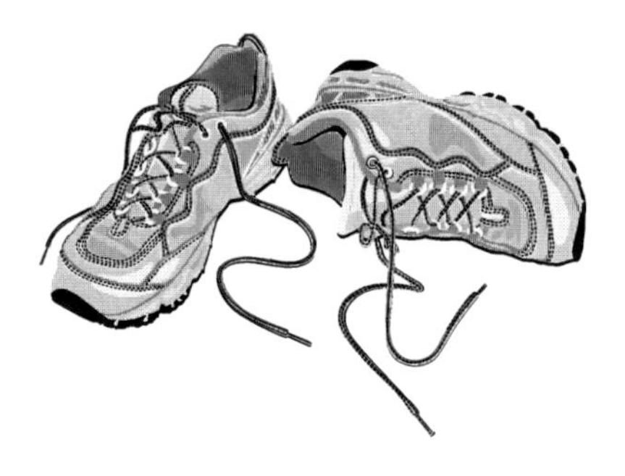

DECEMBER

A LETTER/INVITATION TO THE Gs, to be sent with the DVD, *Racing Against the Clock.*

I wish I were there to talk with you about the DVD. I watched it and thought, "Hey, I can do that." One thing led to another and... I am training to compete in the Rocky Mountain Senior Games. Each state has them. The Colorado ones are June 21-25. Kansas Games are September 21-24.

Mary Ann (my teaching colleague and good friend) is my trainer. She has a doctorate in gerontology and specializes in Physical Activity for Seniors; that's us. I have started my training and like it a lot; this is a surprise to me. The design is gentle and a building process.

I figure I will get into the best shape maybe ever; solidify my children's' notion that I am a bit nuts; impress the heck out of my grandchildren; have a whole new adventure; and get a whole new wardrobe. I am going to run the 100 meter and do the long jump. No, I've never done either. I, like you, have never competed in sports... not available when we grew up. It is exciting to me to think of being an athlete in competition... a new leap at 65.

Why am I telling you this? Oh, you know, don't you? Why not all of us? Why not A "G Team"? Seriously. There are many events... golf, swimming, shot put (!), ping pong... I have included a schedule for Colorado.

Another bonus would be that we would need to get together for some training. Then we could send video tapes back and forth regarding the shape up programs.

We would have to have G Team shirts and G Team colors.

Saragene has already bought in... hey, you old broads, let's go for it!

Oh, and by the way, for people who win in the State Games, there are Senior Olympics in Kentucky in 2007. Can you get an 8 x 10 glossy of that!

I await your responses!!!

Love to each,

I haven't sent this letter/invitation yet. I think it's about, "If I don't send it, they can't say no."

December 4

I have had children at home. A joy to hear of youngest son James' preferences in legal cases. I like knowing that he, as an attorney, is impatient with people who spend their time and money scrapping with neighbors over stupid meaningless things like how tall a fence is or, even worse, how wide the pickets are. People who spend time and energy and resources on revenge need to get a life. I worry about the world and particularly our country. A recent newspaper article devoted several columns and pictures to how people "get even." There were pictures of people, all smiling, telling their favorite jabs at people they consider rude. So the man who was irritated at a barking dog in his neighborhood whistles loudly until the owner calls the dog in. Then there was the man who picked up the neighbor dog's poop and sneaked it onto the neighbor's porch where "hopefully he'll step in it." It's the You-bug-me-and-I'll-bug-you-louder approach. There was the person who told a phone solicitor to "hold on a second" and then put the phone down and left it, explaining, "I can use up some of their time like they use up mine." There is clearly no appreciation for a person trying to earn, probably, minimum wage by making these calls. Why not say, "No, thanks" and hang up?

Why not bother to get on a No Call list?

This article went on to advise "the foot soldiers of life's smallest battles" to be careful in their payback schemes (that was the phrase used) and not do something that "can get you sued." Somewhere, the article mentioned "deliciously devious ways to get back at people." AND there is actually a Rejection Hotline. Instead of telling someone you don't want to see them or meet them, you give them a number to call and some stranger, for a fee, tells them!

I do think that our society is losing many things, including kindness to each other.

Shape Up Journal December 6

My leg hurts. Last night I sat in a Jacuzzi and aimed the jets at the muscles that apparently are the culprits. M.A. says they are the adductors or abductors – no, probably not. I then got a directed massage, including tiger balm, in the hurting areas. And today it hurts as much or more. Not sore as from too much emphasis there… just the old soreness. If this ache/pain stuff kicks up regularly when I walk, how am I to run and jump? Sometimes I think I may be a ridiculous old woman pretending that I am going to be able to do this.

I have just consciously realized that when I get a bit down and then do some of my exercises, my mood lifts. I guess I knew what I was talking about when I told my depressed psychotherapy clients that exercise is an anti-depressant.

On a more positive note I can now stand in The Stork with one leg up, balancing on the other foot for a count of 20; I can do lunges with little effort; and am sometimes able to answer questions like, "Where do you need to stretch?" and "Where do you feel that?" At first, I just looked kind of blank and truly could not identify specifics in my body. Now, sometimes I can. Whatever that means is fascinating to me, that I could lose touch with my body.

That same body changed in 1975 when I had a radical mastectomy, the treatment of choice for breast cancer in that time.

Super Woman Phase I

After my first breast cancer diagnosis in 1975 I read and learned about visualization. It fit for me. I had good guy white cells who were Shogun Warriors recalled from a very fat book, *Shogun*. My Shogun Warriors were strong and wore those black toe slippers that are popular in Japan. Those warriors were so devoted to their skills that they practiced every day, perfecting their techniques to, in my visualization, destroy and get rid of the bad cancer cells and walk gently around the good cells. They were directed in their exercises and maneuvers by General MacArthur. I had read a biography of him. He was many things, including organized and attentive to details. I wanted him on my team for those skills. I felt strong and involved in my body when I used those visualization techniques. Can anyone prove that visualization works? I know that I felt better and that I was exerting some control when I used it.

Control is a major issue for many people with cancer. Someone with cancer can lose control quickly. Medical appointments – many of them – take over your calendar. There's your primary care physician, the oncologist, the radiation doctor, the radiation techs, the chemo nurse, the X-ray techs, the blood takers, the surgeon… and on and on. It can feel like people, machines, and chemicals take your time, your energy, your strength, your normal bodily functions… and on and on. So, sometimes, for some people, things like meditation, visualization, prayer, counseling, etc. can give back a modicum of control. Visualization and counseling helped me.

(Reading back over that last bit, I can hear myself lecturing to the nursing students I taught.)

A "benefit" I derived from that breast cancer

was learning about psychotherapy. I was afraid I was going to die. I wasn't ready to; but my main fears centered on my children who were two and a half, four, and six years old. I was frantic at the thought of leaving them and having them lose their mother. That fear led me into some serious depression, and that depression led me to psychotherapy. I liked it. A lot. So when I, with some skilled guidance from my therapist, Mila, was able to climb out of the worst of the depression, I decided to go to graduate school and get a degree in Counseling Psychology so I could do therapy.

I was 37 years old, had one breast, and was still very much into being and doing everything. I now think that my Type A behavior was one of the contributing factors in my developing cancer. Research has shown that stress is often a factor in many, if not most, illnesses and diseases. I continued my role as a Super Woman; I went to graduate school full-time with three young children. We had just moved into a new home which we were redecorating from top to bottom. My husband and children were supportive. I taught Tommy, who was by then eight years old, to do the wash (never touching any of my clothes, of course) and the four and six year old to sort and fold laundry. My husband helped with just about everything except cooking and adjusted his schedule to cover much of the child care. We also had a neighbor whom we dubbed "St. Joan" who had baby-sat for the boys since they were born. I owe what sanity I maintained to her.

Things were going well. I liked my graduate school classes and the stimulation of being in school as an adult. As a 1958 freshman at the University of Kansas (Rock Chalk Jayhawk!) I actually received a double F at mid-term in Hellenistic History and was on academic probation. In graduate school, I got all A's.

So it was that after having several "suspicious" breast lumps and several breast biopsies I agreed to have a prophylactic/preventative subcutaneous mastectomy. That is where the surgeon removes about 90% of the tissue of the breast, puts an implant in, and retains the skin and nipple. I had that implant for more than 20 years before I slipped on an uneven sidewalk in Isla Mujeres, Mexico, (ironic to be in Isle of Women, huh?), rammed that side of my chest into a light pole… well, that's a whole other story. Now I just have a flat chest which I prefer to that uneven one. My first choice would be to have two breasts; but on my good news days I can say that at least my breast prostheses will never sag, even when I'm 80.

Super Woman Phase II

I chose to have that subcutaneous mastectomy during Winter Break and to complete an Extra Credit project on pain control using visualization. Who was this driven person?

When the plastic surgeon came in for his pre-surgery consult, I told him my plan to use visualization for healing. Many doctors in the 70's pooh-poohed "alternative therapies" and responded to them with a raised eyebrow and an accompanying smirk; so I only shared my plan because I had some questions about the surgical procedure he would be doing. I needed to know some specifics about where I might hurt and what the healing process should be at its maximum. Then my visualization could be more specific. Amazingly enough, he didn't visibly smirk, and he answered my questions. I planned my visualization, using my Samurai warriors and General MacArthur again.

The plastic surgeon came in for one more visit after I was awake, post-op. He came in, alone, and told me that an unexpected result had occurred. They found two primary malignant tumors in that let's-just-take-it-out-for-safety breast.

"Two primary tumors"

"Malignant"

He delivered that news from the door; said

I should consult an oncologist; then left the room. I was alone in that room.

The next specialist, an oncologist, did it differently. After seeing all the reports he told me that although I was undoubtedly upset, the good news was that I had just had the perfect surgery for a condition I didn't know I had.

"Good news"

"Perfect surgery for the condition"

My husband went out for Chinese food and champagne so we could celebrate. The nurses came in smiling and added to the mood. I tell this story to my classes of nursing students. Little things, like the oncologist's re-frame, can make a big difference. I have often wished that that doctor would travel from med school to med school around the country and teach other doctors to deliver bad news with both honesty and hope.

I need to recall my visualization skills and use them in this training for the Senior Games.

December 11

Our friends, the Kohlmans, treated us to a Christmas concert which was a marvelous mixture of traditional music with special touches. Imagine "Away in a Manger" as a jazz piece; it was beautiful and didn't seem like a stretch. Before the program began Linda K. and I were catching up. She asked about my training program. I told her that I had backed off a bit because I was having problems with my leg. As I was describing the problems and paused, we both said in unison, "Oh, a sports injury!" We laughed at the "paragraph" we had just spoken in those words. It was one more validation from a my-decade friend that only now can we indulge in such activities and earn a "sports injury." Now I must really belong. Fun and funny and somewhat enlightening regarding a subject I had never given much attention to. Maybe I could become athletic and like it.

Having a whole new experience at age 65 is just what I need. On the one hand, this journal documentation feels egocentric. On the other hand, Mary Ann Kluge, PhD, assures me that we are, in addition to entertaining me, doing research. That's cool too.

December 22

Oh dear. Mary Ann showed me a new exercise for my StepUps, which I finally had the rhythm for and feel confident about.

I can't do this new StepUp thing yet, but it involves stepping up and then down and then into a lunge and then up again. When M.A. does it she looks like a machine. And, yes, cliché though it be, a well-oiled one. I am thunderstruck at the fluidity, the strength, the pace, the perfect coordination. I remember that she has been an elite athlete, an All American in three sports, a college coach.

What in the world am I doing? I have never thought that I could do/be like her athletically, but I cannot put into words the chasm, the Grand Canyon depth, the oceanic spread, the space in the universe I suddenly felt about my athletic ability and hers.

I can't do that StepUp thing even once, slowly.

But I will.

Just not now.

on training for the senior games
a TIGHT program

my thighs especially are tight
I'd like to think it is about ravenous sex
(it's not)

my neck is tight
from hours of kissing
(not really)

after all, I'm sixty-five
and, heaven (as well as my children) knows
grandmothers don't do those things

it is okay though even with my children
to wear tights

so I got these really cool tights
black with silver inserts

and with no underwear
I will be leaping into the sand
I may be leaping out of my decade
and almost flying
in my totally terrific, torrid, tantalizing, and
really, really tight tights

TA DAH!!!! DRUM ROLLLLLLLLLLLLLL

I got THE TIGHTS for a Christmas present. I am clear that I will run faster in these tights. They are black with silver inserts. Truly, only an athlete would wear these tights.

December 30

This morning I read about a girl in Ethiopia who has started running. Running is a way for her to escape. Staying at home with her family would result in her being married, to someone of her parents' choice, and having children, possibly at 13 or 14 years of age. If she runs well she can be in a running club and can actually attend school instead.

My running is self-absorbed and luxurious in contrast.

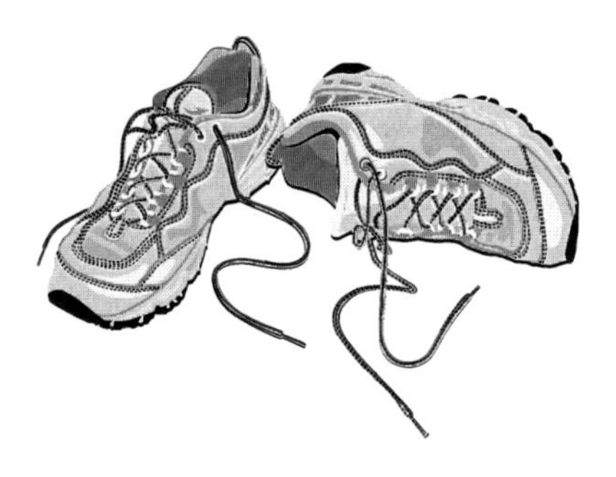

JANUARY 2006

some early day in January

Mary Ann says I am doing really well and that she's impressed at how much I am doing. I, on the other hand, feel that I am not keeping up. I think that getting my Log Sheets in a format that works for me will help me keep track of when I exercise and what I do. Right now I find the sheets confusing. I hope I will not disappoint anyone. M.A. has monthly plans for me to build first my balance, agility and basic strength and then to move to running and eventually jumping. It seems a smart and wise plan.

My feet are sore, especially the left one. M.A. says it is important to exercise the many parts of my feet before I ask them to run and jump. It makes sense. But they (the feet) are rejecting the plan.

And my right leg hurts some almost every

day. Sometimes at night. Almost always when I try to walk even a half mile. I am doing my stretches.

another January day

Today Mary Ann and I walked all over the campus putting up flyers about our Culture and Health course that did not get into the university's spring catalog. Mary Ann noted that my stride has changed. I didn't know this. She is definite and pleased that I am now "leading" with my knees. She was downright exultant that "the exercises are working." She is so very clever to have designed them to use and strengthen the muscles I need for running and jumping… without my running and jumping.

Tom, our oldest, called this evening. Just checking in. Tom is in the business side of professional sports. He regularly meets NBA stars, major league baseball icons, etc. I wonder what he thinks about my athletic endeavors. I haven't asked him; I'm not sure why.

A Bad Day

My trainer and I went to a track today. We warmed up our muscles (with Ice Cream Cones, Knee Circles, Hula Hoops, etc.) and then walked around the whole track once. Then again, fast walking for 100 meters. My feet seemed to want to leave the ground with the fast walking. I "recovered" (meaning got my breath back) and then wanted to run. I started to run, when, with no warning and absolutely no control, I started leaking. To be clear, I was dribbling urine. Actually it felt like a mild stream. I was horrified. I kept running, but my mind could not stay with my legs. I lost all running concentration, wondering and worrying if the urine was running down my leg. I was wearing tights – thank goodness, not the Killer Tights. My mind was racing, but my legs were not.

That finished the workout for me. When I got back to the house I discovered that I had not leaked nearly as much as I thought. That is good, but that it happened at all was a blow.

Who do I think I am?

I am 65. Am I pretending I'm 25?

Am I ridiculous in my tights? Killer Tights. Yeah, right. Will I need to wear a pad? Old Lady with Bladder Problem Trying To Be Young Again. I don't think that I'm 25. The fact is that age, for me, became amorphous after 40. I know that I'm 65. But facts and feelings do not always jibe. I am stuck-in a good way-in my 40's. Most of the time if I were to do a body and mind check and attach an age I would "feel" 42-45. But not today.

Not today at the track.

And there's my leg. The right one. It hurts right now. How interesting that pain seems so much more prominent in bad times.

Is this whole thing crazy?

Early January

I finally mailed all of the stuff to the Gs. I sent the *Racing Against The Clock* DVD, a letter of explanation, the dates and schedules for the Senior Games in Colorado and Kansas and ideas on how we could keep in touch and meet a few times regarding our training. I reallyreallyreally want them to do it.

I am not writing down all the dates any more. I am doing my training regularly. I do the interval training which I now call Pyramids, counting steps of 20, 30, 40, 40, 30, 20. Walk as fast as I can; recover; do the next set; recover; etc. I also am doing intervals of walking fast for one minute and recovering for two minutes. I have tried to add the Nostril Breathing more regularly. The warm-ups are totally second nature now as are many of the exercises. It is enlightening to feel the differences. When I first started the balance ones (standing like a stork on one leg), I could only hold a foot up for about four seconds. Now I can do it for 20 seconds. I think I wrote that in another entry… I am proud.

And the Elevators show distinct improvement and are not even hard any more. The Elevator is when I sit down on a bench and then, with my back straight and no help from my arms, begin to stand up, a few inches at a time. Each few inches up is like going up to a floor on an elevator. I can stop, clearly strengthening my quads as I do so, 8-12 times before I am totally upright. I then go down that same number of "floors" until I gently reach the bench with my butt. At first, I plopped down. No longer. My legs have muscles and are getting much stronger than they have been, probably for many years. I also have begun to notice women who look about my age who plop into a chair and then can get up only by holding on to something. I am so glad I am getting stronger.

January

I made an appointment with a durable medical equipment place which is on my provider list. I want new, lighter weight breast prostheses for sports bras. I am excited about looking for sports bras with pockets for my prostheses. They look comfortable as well as what an athlete would wear! Ahhh… my two years are not up. My insurance company will replace prostheses only after two years. I wonder what a woman is to do if her prostheses get stolen, or lost in luggage, or burned in a house fire. Rules are rules; and our HMOs make our rules.

Of course there was the time a few years back, after the surgical removal of my implanted breast prosthesis, when I then needed two prostheses for my bras instead of one. Breast prostheses cost from $200-$500 each. Companies quit making certain styles and sizes, and, as a matter of fact, no longer made the shape and size I had one of. Silly me: I wanted my two breasts to match! My request for two breast prostheses was denied because our health care policy allowed "one prosthesis each two-year period." When I talked with one of the customer service people at the HMO, she was clear that this "allowance" also referred to artificial legs or arms as well as breasts. That was one time I did not accept such an absurd decision from my HMO. I followed the procedures to challenge their decision. The first step was a letter to their Review Board. My request was denied at that level. My next option was to have a phone interview with a panel of "health care professionals" in their organization. That panel granted that I could order two matching (!) breast prostheses and the insurance company would cover the cost but only as an exception. From then on I could only get one breast prosthesis every so many years. By the time I needed to fight that policy again, the policy had changed. I must not have been the only person who fought them on that.

January 15

Walked one mile on track and did some fast minutes. Four of them.

January 17

Did my warm-ups and then walked one+ miles. Fast minutes twice and intervals 30, 40, 50, 40, 30.

January 18

Same as 17th

January 19

ALL my exercises and stretches. Talked to one of the Gs… she said she can hardly wait. I am encouraged.

January 22

All my exercises and stretches. Takes 45 minutes. I FEEL GOOD.

January 24

I did most of my exercises but nothing that was too strenuous. I didn't eat much dinner.

Woke at midnight with unusual and severe chest and back pain. Went to the Emergency Room for five hours. EKG, CT scan, blood work. The doctor ruled out a heart attack and finally gave a probable diagnosis of acid reflux. Hmm. I will take pills. It hurt a lot. It hurt so much I couldn't describe it. It was like my brain didn't have the space to call up words as it was spending all of its energy experiencing that pain. (Probably, technically, brains don't experience pain… but anyway… that's how I thought about it all later.) John, "my son, the doctor," thinks I should have a stress test just to make sure my heart is okay. As I was lying in the ER (cold of course… why is it always cold there?), after the pain subsided to the point that my brain could entertain thoughts, I thought that a heart attack could really screw up my training for the Senior Games. The thought of a heart attack for me is not on my radar screen. Those things happen to other people. Older people. I do know I'm 65, but a heart attack?

I read somewhere that if you are having chest pain and decide to go to an ER that you should go in an ambulance since the hospital staff responds more quickly to a gurney from an ambulance than from a walk-in. There is then the question of "who pays for the ambulance if you go to the ER and they don't admit you and you don't die?" Answer: I do.

January 25

Massage day. Nice.

January 26

Did I do nothing or did I forget to write it down? Surely the latter.

January 27

Mary Ann suggested that I interview The Gs as to why they do not want to do the Senior Games. I am trying to forget their responses.

January 28

Well! Today I told Mary Ann that a couple of the exercises seem too easy. I wasn't trying to brag; (I can brag and do so unabashedly about my sons and grandchildren) but I just keep increasing reps on my Windmills and Elevators.

She said that I must be ready for something harder for those particular muscles. She gave me a four pound medicine ball (I don't know why they're called that) and I did my Elevators holding that. No big deal.

Next she gave me one of those big bouncy exercise balls that you sit on. I was to put the ball on the wall, hold it there in the small of my back, and then do Elevators. I could do that too! My legs are getting strong. I have to keep myself from asking strangers if they want to feel the muscles in my legs.

M.A. then brought out her balancing pads. I don't know the real name but they are these round shaped-like-a-pancake things that you stand on. They are filled with air and are the size of large over-stuffed Frisbees. The underside looks like a porcupine with a flat-top haircut. The topside is smooth. I am to stand on them and try to do my warm-ups (Ice Cream Cones, Knee Circles, Hula Hoops, etc.) The pads I stand on move and I have to catch my balance, which I can often do.

I remember when my children were learning to skip. Skipping is a big step for little kids. I remember their pride when they got the jump just right. That is how I feel. I am almost like a little kid learning these new physical skills. And when I get one right and then can do it better, I am proud. And pleased. And smiling.

Who ever thought this would be so rewarding?

Then we walked with Pyramids. I did 30, 40, 50, 60, 50, 40, 30. Easy. Then I ran but not sprinted for a minute. When M.A. noted later that for the first time in our walks I was not yawning, I realized that my breathing is improving also. She explained that the yawning occurs as a result of not breathing quite right.

I'll have to ask more about that another time.

I have a Right Leg report. It has stopped hurting. Totally. Completely. Everywhere. I have been to a chiropractor four times now. What he does seems akin to voodoo, poking me with something and then causing his "table" to pound (gently) under my body. Next, he does an "adjustment" by scrunching some parts of my body. I do not intend to make fun of, rather, to try to describe what makes little sense to me. For the first time in many months I have had six whole days of no leg pain. I don't care what he does or how unlikely it may seem or if my primary care physician will not give me a referral to a chiropractor (and she won't) I will take it and gladly pay what is actually a modest fee. So there.

Pat, the massage therapist I have seen twice a month for several years now, gave me a stretching exercise for my feet. The only sore area left on my foot is definitely getting better also. Although I have not articulated this before, I think that trying different treatment modalities and then keeping what works makes perfect sense. Drugs, exercise, acupuncture, goat's blood – whatever works.

Some Thoughts

I keep thinking about The Gs. I looked through these journal notes and realized that I have not written about their to-a-person emails, bailing. Even Saragene. I am disappointed for me, and I am disappointed for them. I wish they were having some of the positive experiences and feelings that I am having. A big piece of how positive this feels is Mary Ann. What I mean is that Mary Ann is an extremely positive person, period. She is not Mary Sunshine, and she is genuinely and sincerely positive. She is also well-versed in exercise physiology and has particular interest and expertise in older adults. She regularly tells me that I am doing so well and that she thinks my attitude and progress are amazing, even better than she anticipated. I believe her, and there is a self-fulfilling prophecy aspect for me when I hear her comments.

I think I may have just realized something else new. I am on a high. (I may be sounding like Mary Sunshine.) I think I am getting an endorphin boost. Cool. I should be tired from what I did today. Instead, I am pumped; I have not had these experiences before.

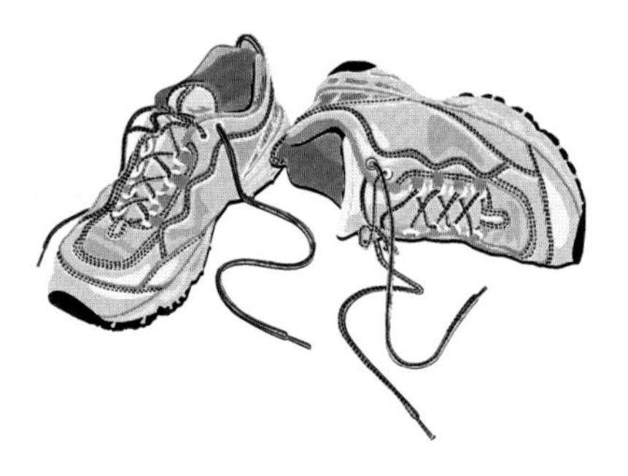

FEBRUARY 2006

A daily log seems superfluous since it is now ordinary to exercise regularly. There are several February highlights.

I went to a Yoga week-end at a Franciscan Retreat in the woods. It was fantastic. The structure that Teryl, the instructor, provided seemed just right except for getting up so early; but I even accepted that and went to sleep early also. I actually loved the waking up part which was someone (a volunteer participant) who went thru the halls tapping this Asian bell thing which was so gentle it seemed like waking up to a dream. Ting. Ting. Ting, ting, ting. I want an alarm clock that has that as an alarm; Teryl says there are such things. Ten of us gathered for our early morning Yoga session of about an hour or so. Time seemed to pass at a slower rate than in my usual days. The nuns at the Franciscan retreat served our meals which we ate in silence. Time to walk. Journaling time.

I felt calm. Centered. I want to keep much of that feeling.

Before this Yoga retreat I had only done a bit of Yoga by watching a DVD. At the retreat I did pretty well with most of the positions. I could not hold them as long or as tall or as deep as some of the other people, but I stretched and paid attention to my body. There was a labyrinth in the woods at the retreat center. I had seen a small labyrinth in Santa Fe and had seen references to labyrinths but didn't grasp the concept. I wrote a poem about labyrinths in our lives.

a labyrinth

Can I spell it?
Can I do it?

Sure, I can walk it
but my question is
What should my question be?

As I begin to see the trees
erect, reposed, weeping, proud, angled,
leaning so I may pass
I repeat some patterns
and wonder if I am stuck
destined to repeat the circles of my life

With attention to the path
I experience new space

The turns are not always gentle
Yet I can go into them gently
seeing thing I've viewed before
seeing them new

I may have passed this path before
not noticing

Noticing now
that even when curves seem sudden or severe
Even then I may enter gently and peacefully
open to new possibilities in old paths

No matter the spelling
I walk it
Labyrinth

Every time we had quiet time for reflection I seemed to write a poem. The most amazing thing, though, is that when the group got back together I shared the poem I had just written. I usually do not do that. It was nice. And oddly, I think that somehow the new me – the me who is training for the Senior Games – feels more confident. Not necessarily that my poetry is good (although I do think that some of it is), but that I am who and what I am and in comfortable, safe situations with people I trust to understand… I can be who and what I am more often.

Tall Dormant Thistle Things

I tried to talk to plants today.
First I named them.

Then they introduced themselves.

I acknowledged their naming
and they told me more.

One had died
and was still being embraced by the family.

Young ones wandered though not far.
The proud Papa patriarch provided protection.
Grandmother watched, as women do,
a close distance away

I tried to talk to plants today.
I learned a listening lesson.

February 9 was not a good day

I went to a podiatrist about some discomfort on the tops of my feet. Those prominent bones, when touched by shoe parts, still hurt. The podiatrist suggested cortisone shots. I readily agreed to them as I had great relief with cortisone shots in my elbow many years ago and more recently in my shoulder. Well. I had acute pain starting about six hours after the shots, could not wear shoes, could barely walk, and hurt and hurt and hurt. This doctor did not prepare me for any of that. It was four days before my feet were almost back to their normal hurting; and the bill was almost $800. "Insurance" paid it. Isn't that us?

I went to a Y for a Senior Fitness Test. My results were, to my mind, mediocre. Hmm.

February 20: A Medical Report

I had a Stress Test and Echocardiogram as a follow-up to my ER visit. As I waited for results the only thing that worried me was that I wasn't worried. I just want to keep up with my training. Go figure.

I guess I am fine except that I also have Mitral Valve Prolapse which no one seems too concerned about. Then there's my over-active bladder, osteopenia, acid reflux, and high cholesterol. Three prescriptions, extra calcium, gelatin for my nails, a multi-vitamin, pills for acid reflux, and an aspirin a day. Are these the rewards for aging? What happened to wisdom?

Ruminations

I am not sure how much of what I do is for

or about me. I do not see myself as a people-pleaser, and I doubt many would ascribe those words to me. Yet, I am very aware that with this training for the Senior Games I like the attention I get, and I want my trainer (and friend) to be proud of me. I also want my children and grandchildren to be impressed at my performance. And when I say performance, I mean winning. So what does that make me? Therapy is fun and interesting and usually worthwhile, and I don't need to analyze any of that. Just thinking.

February 24 is a great day

My granddaughter Sam's attempt at the long jump.

I went to Virginia to have a few days with Sam, my four year old grand-daughter. What a total joy being a grandmother is. Of course I feel responsible for her safety when she is with me, but I am not responsible for her manners, her toilet training (earlier of course), her eating habits, her homework (later of course), and so on. I just get to be with her and love her and delight in her and have the time for all of that. I have three other grandchildren, Charlie, Ted, and Maisy, who are equally wonderful.

I feel as if some of my genes/my values/ my experiences and feelings/my thoughts and words could keep on happening as my grandchildren have grandchildren, etc. Those kinds of thoughts are new to me, a factor I suppose of aging. Being a grandmother has also made me cry more easily, in a good way though.

My 10 year old granddaughter Maisy has started track for the first time. She is doing the 100meter and the long jump. I am not sure that she consciously has chosen the same events I am doing. I am so pleased and proud. I've always heard that twins often skip a generation; I guess long jumps do too.

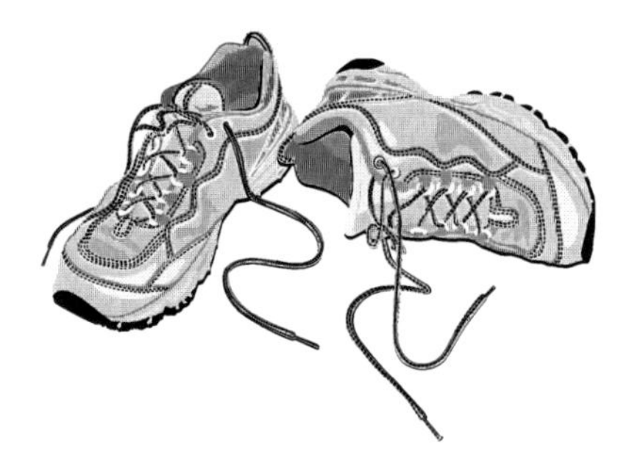

MARCH

March 2: A good news/bad news day

The good news is that Mary Ann and I arrived in Cabo San Lucas in Mexico today, a non-stop three hour flight from Denver. The bad news is that I almost died this evening.

Okay, so I tend to be dramatic.

And I really and truly almost drowned.

The man on the bus from the Aeroporto was "not trying to sell us anything." Rather, he wanted to invite us for an all-you-can-eat breakfast buffet and just to hear about the Westin Resort BUT with no obligation AND we could get a free taxi back to the Aeroporto when we leave AND a free dinner at some nice restaurant AND two free activities of our choice EVEN INCLUDING parasailing. ALL IN ALL about $400 worth of stuff AND he doesn't want to sell us anything. Riiiight. (A sidebar here is that we actually did all of that and Mary Ann

BOUGHT A TIME SHARE!)

I digress. This same man told us useful facts about Cabo San Lucas. One such fact is that the ocean on the Pacific side has a very strong undertow and one should not swim or even wade there.

Well, sure you wouldn't try to swim, but when the sun is setting and the tide is just starting to come in, it is totally inviting to just get your feet wet. It was kind of cold and felt good. We were not wading; we were just barely getting our feet wet. And looking at the sunset. And talking. And not paying much attention to the ocean.

It happened so fast. A powerful rogue wave took my feet away, knocking me over. I fell onto my side and was deluged with ocean. M.A. grabbed me and said, "I've got you." Still with no feet under me, I scrambled and frantically, flailing, tried to right myself. Mary Ann looked up and saw an even bigger wave coming and yelled, "Get up! Get up now and GO! GO! GO!" She was holding me up and pulling me; I did get my feet under me and went as fast as I could, stumbling up the wet, steep, sand incline. Mary Ann ran right behind me.

Mary Ann saved my life.

It was more than an hour before I felt fear. M.A. said that if I hadn't gotten up and moved quickly up that steep hill of sand we both would have been swept out by that second wave. Two fishermen had seen our struggle and hurried to where we were to see if we were alright. At least there would have been some record of our disappearance.

We had been in Mexico for five hours, and I almost drowned. If my legs were not as strong as they are from my exercises I doubt that I could have gotten up and run so quickly and strongly from that second wave.

I have an answer ready for James Dobson, should I ever meet him.

I was drowning and YES I AM SAVED

i am safe

splashed
soaked
sandy
scrambled
shored

with
several seconds
of freeze frames
labeled indelibly
in the album of my mind

So if, when that first wave swept my feet and legs away and landed me on my side, M.A. had not grabbed me and held me up I would have swallowed water, panicked, and.....

The if's and if not's in our lives determine our lives.

And our deaths.

I am having a hard time leaving this subject since I'm remembering that I really did come within a foot of death. Drowning. Of all ways for me to die.

My watch still works and lights up and everything, but Mary Ann's favorite flip-flops are somewhere in the Pacific.

March 4

Today is my mother's birthday. She would be 96. She would be glad that I'm still alive. I wish I had asked her more questions. When did she start her period? Was she scared? What did her mother tell her? When did she start menopause? What did she think about Pearl Harbor? And Hiroshima? Was that really hard? How long was my Dad in Europe? What kinds of things did she think and do when he was in the army in 1944? What were her favorite parts of life? What didn't she get to do that she had always hoped for? And many more questions.

In retrospect, I guess I thought there would be time for that, that she would not die so quickly with not even a moment for good-bye.

A FEW IF NOTS

I parasailed today

If I were not 65
And if I were not clear
That death can sweep in quickly
I would not have

I may get a tattoo too

Why Now?

Had you asked me on any one day of my 65 years if I ever wanted to parasail, the answer would have been a guffaw followed by a resounding "No way!" So, why now? I am not at all sure that I have an answer, but it is something about doing new things and having new confidence and somewhat of a new identity. It was like being a bird, and I wasn't even scared. At least not much.

Cavorting in Cabo

moving, breathing, squiggling, circling, swinging, stretching, elongating, walking, walking fast, jogging, counting, running, sprinting, timing, leaping, landing, measuring

I ran in the sand today. In my sneakers. On flat sand. The greater thing is that I leapt. I did several things right, albeit, unintentionally:

I took off (like running fast); I drove my arms forward (like in my StepUps).

I kept my headlights, which is what Mary Ann calls breasts, up (like in my lunges) and I landed solidly on both feet (like my elevators).

My coach was impressed. She says I have Muscle Memory which is a highly descriptive term and an incredible something. I have apparently trained my muscles with my regular exercises, which Mary Ann designed specifically to lead to running and leaping; so when I do actions that mimic those exercises, my muscles have learned the motions needed for those activities and remember the motion and balance needed. It's like being on autopilot.

I have begun to think more about my body. I am only recently aware that I have taken my body for granted and that I am fortunate and blessed that the parts have worked so well. I am now more appreciative and want to honor and tend to those parts—the muscles, the bones, and the ligaments although, truth be told, I still do not get what ligaments are and do. I am, however, clear that I actively love mine now.

When we got back from Cabo San Lucas, I saw what Mary Ann had filmed of my training on the beach. Our TV screen is bigger than I realized. Big. And that's how I looked. Big. Old people – a category I have not put myself in – have this saggy bottom thing. I don't know what happens anatomically, but bottoms sag. Well, lots of things sag, but the bottom thing is particularly troublesome for me. So there I am, on video, cavorting in the sand in Cabo San Lucas, trying to long jump for the first time ever and even though the distance was puny, feeling good for the effort. Then I saw the film and saw a saggy bottom, even in spandex. Depressing.

I re-read that and first thought that I must be terribly vain; perhaps I am. That possibility does not, however, influence a totally separate factor: bodies age and change and begin to look old even when we do many of the right things. That is obvious as I write it now, and I think I've been operating under a wishful delusion. I have not thought about sagging bottoms specifically relating to me before. The downside (to excuse a pun about bun) is that it sags; the upside is that I am still upright.

And while on the subject of Body Betrayal I want to say a few words about hair. I could understand and perhaps even accept if, with age, I got more hair or less hair. But to get more hair on my face to the tune of a mustache and sideburns and less hair in my pubic area so I look like a newborn small animal down there—that makes no sense and seems unfair. I recently read that shaving down there is popular with younger women. Sounds itchy to me. I am okay with not having, hardly ever, to shave my legs or under my arms, but what's the deal with nose hair? For 65 years I did not need to pay the slightest attention to the hair in my nose. Now I have to have a little buzzing instrument to trim my nose hair. At least I do not look like I have broccoli growing out of my ears as Tom, our eldest, describes some older men. The ear hair does seem to happen mostly to men. Small favors.

Not Always A Choice

Where before was bare
I now have hair

In my nose
And on my chin

In this aging game
Is there no win?

My bottom sags
My breathing lags
My hearing wanes
The only gains

Seem to be pounds
Put on my hips
And furry stuff
Above my lips

For now at least
I'll take this choice
Albeit with
A whining voice

Clear for now
Just short of breath
I prefer these woes
To the length of death

As for death in general, I find that my schedule allows its presence more in the last few years. It seems, as I talk with other friends my age, that a bit more time spent with the death subject is age-related. It's not as though I spend days or even hours thinking about dying or even worrying about dying. Odd things—thinking about Maisy or Sam being a mother and smiling at the thought and then realizing that I probably will not actually see those days; or having a lightening-strike pain in my head for a mini-second and wondering if this is it, the way I will die, and if not I'd better get all of those old photos organized. Then there are some of my things. Will anyone remember the silver pin with Edelweiss on it, the pin I bought for my mother because her father wore Edelweiss in his lapel in his wedding picture in 1900? Will anyone notice that in the wedding picture on my bedroom wall?

I have things left undone. I have always wanted to write each son a letter (to be opened after my death, in tears, I would hope) explaining why he is and always has been my favorite. And I could make a case for each one. I better write those.

I'm pretty darn sure I did not think about things like that until very recently. I don't get depressed about my death; I'm simply aware that it will occur.

Apparently, though, I have lucked out another day; this is a day to go to the track.

Back to that saggy video footage from Cabo – when I told M.A. how I felt about looking big and saggy in the film she responded with what I came to know is another characteristic which makes her an excellent trainer: "Well, okay then. Don't look at that footage any more. We will look at all of it after the games and you will see the progress that I have seen and see every day. Just keep doing what you've been doing. You are amazing."

I couldn't even remember what I was upset about.

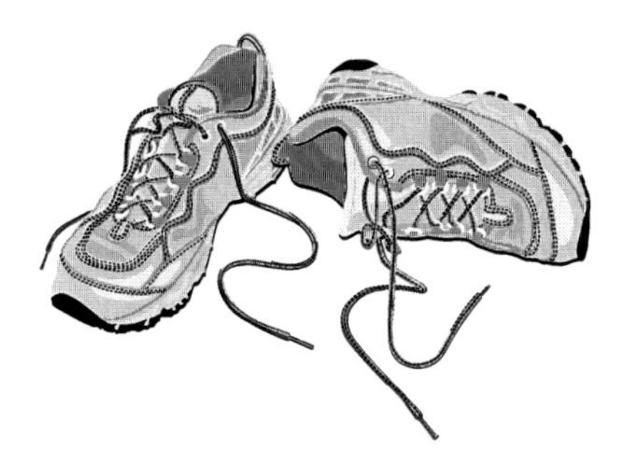

APRIL

Early April

Mary Ann just read me a possible beginning for an article she is working on. (She works more than I do.) She is applying theory to what I am doing and how I am doing it. That is intellectually interesting but not of personal interest to me. I chuckle thinking about such phrases as, "Don't let the facts get in the way of your convictions." In this instance I am not the least bit concerned whether or not theories regarding physical activity seem to fit with what I am doing. After the fact, such information is of interest to me. But not in the middle.

Freud Again?

An interesting inner dialogue. At first my intellect wanted to get into shape because that is a healthy thing to do. Then my ego liked telling people that I was training for the Senior

Games. My super-ego began to be proud at my increased strength and agility. My id chimed in when I neglected my exercises with some blame and guilt.

But today… today, my body yearned to exercise. Almost like when I'm thirsty. I was pretty pleased.

Still the First Week in April

We found a track and after some warm-ups I ran the 100 and did some jumps in the sand pit. I was slow and short in distance and later sore. My trainer took responsibility for not warming me up enough. I am discouraged. My time for the 100 is lousy: still 24 seconds. My jumping is pathetic. Why did I think I could long jump? I don't have long anythings in my whole body. I just have about two more months. I guess I will improve. But, enough?

Still

I went, by myself for the first time, to the track today to train. M.A. was out of town. I had my slip of paper to remind me how to warm up. Walk around once. Then stretch, being certain to do lunges. Then do whole track in eighths with walking for an eighth, knees high stepping, walking, butt kicks, walking, jogging, etc. alternating these. After that I set up my plastic cones/markers to tell me where to start running my fastest and when to slow down again as I completed the 100m. This felt different to me than any times before. When I clicked into running my fastest, I actually felt a click. It was almost like a switch had been turned on. I felt strong and fast. I did it again and felt that same shift into high gear. I may be okay at this. I have two more months to train.

Saturday, about April 7?

The weather has been psychotic, so I have been exercising inside until today. Even today it was windy. At the track I did the usual warm-ups and then some sprints. I felt slow and was slow. I felt too tired to jump, but the sand pit was there so I tried. I jumped 7+ feet which is quite an improvement and encouraging. Mary Ann gave me several technique pointers. I didn't know that I should run as fast as I can before I jump. I was sort of loping. And I am to lead with one leg and bring the other one up to follow. I think I thought I was to jump with both feet together. I am mostly concentrating on learning and improving, but I regularly note what a good coach can do. Mary Ann gave me exercises that "fit" jumping, so part of that process just happens now when I jump. Only after I get over a bit of intimidation about the runway, the line I must not step on or over, and the totally foreign notion of hurling my body into sand – only then does she begin to show me and tell me in words some technique things to consider. I'm certain there will be more information, examples, and demonstrations forthcoming. If all of that had come to me at once I would have been overwhelmed and discouraged at the thought of learning so many new things. She also continues to praise me in ways that sound and feel sincere. I have never thought much (at all?) about what would make a good coach, so that question is a new and fascinating subject for me.

Boy, was I tired. I took sips of water and some power drink, kept moving and did a few stretches, then had a snack within 30 minutes – all the right things. I want to say I felt like a rag doll, but my rag doll self was so soft and floppy that I hardly felt anything. I wasn't sore or sleepy or even tired exactly, not spent like after good sex. I was more like the kind of tired after a transatlantic flight and then Chicago and Customs and then the next flight and then the bags and then the drive home and then literally and finally falling into bed like a too-heavy sack being thudded to the ground. I don't want to moan and whine, and I do want to do this… but I sure wish I had started many years ago.

The Sunday after that Saturday

I woke up this morning with this rhyme

Rhyme of the Morning

i've been a runnin' and a jumpin'
tiny barbells i've been pumpin'

I'm trying to reverse
the arrival of the hearse
I'm not sure which one is worse
being dead or being cursed

With exercises I don't know
Don't lock elbows, fast then slow
Keep knees soft, arms out straight
Don't curl wrists, pump, then wait

Keep knees bent
Squat, then rise
What's that noise?
Moaning thighs

All these skills
i've acquired
Gee, I'm proud
and really tired!

To Florida To Meet The Gs

When I arrived at the gate, the other four Gs were there with hugs and already-experienced funny stories. The condo Saragene arranged for free is perfect space for us with a deck that looks out on some water with fisher people and those long-legged, long-necked, ever-so-graceful birds that Florida produces, lights of the city, and possibly though unseen, some alligators on the grass. I know that we all get accustomed to our surroundings which sometimes include mosquitoes in the mid-west, bears in Colorado, land-slides on the west coast, but alligators? We actually did not see any. I taped a conversation with the Gs to try to understand why they decided not to do the Senior Games. Their responses sounded like weak excuses to me; I

The Gs in Florida: Judy, Karen Saragene, me and Veet.

think I was a little angry.

Whoever owns the condo had StepUp benches and weights in the very room in which I stayed. I privately did my weights and StepUps. Then I jogged in the sand along the beach when we looked for a place for lunch. We found a fun Cuban place, and I introduced the Gs to Mojitos. We had our usual stomach-aching, laughing time, and I had a quiet realization that I was missing my regular training time. While we were in Florida, I got a call from an excited Mary Ann telling me that she and Jackie, another colleague at the university, and I won the Colorado University President's Award for Teaching With Technology. Life is good. I am a lucky woman.

Salt Lake City

Almost immediately after Florida I got on a plane to Salt Lake City for a conference Mary Ann and I were attending. She was a presenter. The hotel had an exercise room. This was the first time that I felt comfortable in an exercise room. When I started my training I sporadically did some free weight exercises with two, three and four pound weights. I was up to eight pound weights and actually knew what to do with them. I also learned to use and set the treadmill. I could do my warm-up exercises on a mat there. There were towels and a water cooler, and TVs. I felt official. Surely now I am an athlete.

Bresses, Bras, and Bag Lady

I haven't talked about one of the big Bennies from all of this: the clothes. I definitely prefer and now have five pairs of tights. They are comfy, stretchy, non-binding, not tight, with nothing to get in the way. I have mid-thigh spandex pants (you really do not want flapping things when you run); wicking underwear and no-tops socks; wicking shirts (sleeveless, short-sleeved/long-sleeved with thumb-holes) of different colors, and two pairs of running shoes. Soon, I hope to add sports bras. This is a challenge which I am still working on. I need pockets for my prostheses and so far I have not found sports bras designed that way.

Those 70s mastectomy bras must have been designed by a large-busted woman who assumed that all of us have "big bresses" as my grand-daughter Maisy once announced about her Mom to a grocery store check-out line. Those mastectomy bras could hold up an elephant. Since I no longer have any "bresses" I could choose any size breast prostheses, and at some point chose to have larger ones—larger than my natural breasts had been. That was kind of fun, but the prostheses felt heavy. For several years, I have bought regular bras and had pockets sewn into them. I could go off on the prices for all of that stuff. The little pockets which are the size of a medium oval-shaped pancake are about twelve dollars each. What a rip-off. Anyway, back to the desire to have a comfy bra with no hooks, soft material, no under-wire, and fabric that wicks. I will get this figured out.

I just remembered the first time, back in 1975 after my first mastectomy, when I asked my breast surgeon about getting a breast form for my bra. He, with a straight face, suggested that I sew some beans in a bag and put that in my bra. Right. That would be funny if he hadn't been serious.

I called the American Cancer Society; a woman from their Reach for Recovery program came to see me in the hospital. (I actually was in the hospital for about a week. Now it seems that even a lung transplant is day surgery.) This woman came in a form-fitting red sweater. I knew that whoever came would be a breast cancer survivor. She walked into that hospital room with two even, matched, normal-looking breasts packed into a red sweater; that was better than any anti-depressant I can imagine. That ACS Reach for Recovery angel volunteer gave me some soft lamb's wool to put in my bra in the first few weeks and gave me all the information I needed to get a breast prosthesis later. No beans.

As for having cancer, I have to add some of the positive results for me. I started looking at life differently at age 35. I quickly grasped the reality that being in my 30s didn't come with any guarantees or warranties. Cliché as it is, I did stop to smell the flowers. For several years, my regular check-ups not only sent me into a spin of worry days before the appointments; they also sent me into a jump-start of joy when the results came back. I was okay. I was cancer free. I still had my life. My husband. My children. And I still had the 8x10 glossy of all the ways any of us could end, any time. Having that realization in the forefront every few months and then once a year when I got to that stage of my check-ups kept me on my toes – the toes that danced and jumped and dared to remember that death can swoop in quickly.

Perhaps at 60 or 65 I would have had those realizations without cancer; I'm not sure. I will not say that I'm glad that I had cancer; I will say that I'm glad that I had those realizations when I did.

Back to now: I have become a bag lady. I now always carry a bag to the track with me. I bought a stop watch which I cannot figure out. I pushed all of the buttons several times, and now it beeps just once every hour on the hour. I have not been able to coax it into any other function. Reliable beeping on the hour is not helpful in timing my sprints. I honestly think I need to fly James (youngest son who is the gadget king) to Colorado to get the stop watch to stop beeping and make it time things; teach us how to switch our new TV from TV to DVD player and back again in under 20 minutes of random button-pushing; change the clock in my car when Daylight Savings Time occurs; and explain what all of the buttons on the "only one remote" do, if anything. Sometimes I need to remind myself that I have a stack of proof from my lived experience that I am an intelligent woman because things like this stop watch thing could make me waver on the smart-me theory.

When I am going to exercise at the track or gym I pack my gym bag and carry, at a minimum, the beeping stop watch along with my running shoes, my running shorts or tights, a top of some kind, my exercise bra, a windbreaker/gloves/thing to keep ears warm (just in case of weather), my cones/markers for the track, a tape measure, the video camera, extra battery, extra film, some deodorant, hair brush and hair wax, cell phone, driver's license and money in a pouch, power bars and drink, and my strap for stretching. And I keep changing my clothes. I used to get dressed for work, or lounging at home, in the morning, and that was it until evening when I got into a nightshirt. Now I am part chameleon, a revolving door of outfits with changes of clothes and shoes two to three times a day from home to class to errands to exercise. What was at first cumbersome now seems normal.

I do love my new athlete clothes and when I showed my really fancy cool killer tights to Hope, at the office, and she said, "Wow, you look like someone you see on TV," I thought all of the changing is worth it.

The clothes do a couple of things:

1. The right clothes are comfortable and do not distract from the work-out
2. The clothes make various statements to the world as well as the wearer. This is true for me and I think for others or sportswear designers would be out of jobs. Some of the messages are: "I have goals;" "I am healthy;" "I am in good shape;" "I am trying to get into shape;" "I am strong;" "I am working hard;" "I am taking care of my body;" "I may be old but I'm not dead;" and my favorite, "Hey, look at my cool clothes!"

It just occurred to me that I often wear my pink hat from the Susan G. Komen Race Day. I have not thought about this much until right now, but I think I also am making a couple of statements:

1. I have had breast cancer and I can still do anything I decide to work at.
2. You can have breast cancer and go on living, and it doesn't have to be a secret.

It is not unusual, when I have that hat on, to pass a woman in a similar hat in a parking lot or at the grocery store and have her give me a thumbs up or smile knowingly, or say, "Me too." That's pretty neat.

almost the end of April

I need to start my sprint faster so I found the track coach of a nearby college, explained briefly who I am and what I am doing, and asked if I might borrow some starting blocks to practice with. He said, "No, if I loan them to you, I would have to loan them to everyone who asks." I paused and then asked him if he got many requests. He said, "Well… no… but I would have to." Then I called the track coach at my kids' old high school, Cheyenne Mountain, and he said, "Sure."

I called the Rocky Mountain Senior Games again and was told that the time for last year's

100m winner was 18 point something seconds. I have yet to be under 20 seconds. That news discouraged me for awhile; but I am back on track (ha!). We have not really timed me for the whole 100m as I do fast as I can only for the middle section. I need lots of work on starting. My starts are slow and awkward. The starting blocks don't help me much. I'm not sure I even want to mention jumping. It is pathetic. I am committed to improving. I no longer think so much about gold medals. Did I mention that I do not have long legs?

Mary Ann gave me some new exercises, and I'm not sure I'm doing them quite right. I also don't know if I add these to my old ones or substitute these for old ones. I sometimes feel a bit of a bother and dunce for not quickly picking up these new exercises. I do balance those thoughts/feelings with the reality that **I have never done any of this before.** Actually, I need to add some words. Sometimes – not often but sometimes – I don't want to exercise. And it gets all mixed up with doing this for me and/or not disappointing Mary Ann and my other friends who are keeping up on my training efforts. I think that the bottom line is that I do want to do this. I certainly want to get and stay as healthy as I can. What gets to me some times is Mary Ann and her regimens. She walks and runs and bikes and hikes and lifts weights (I mean **weights**) and stretches and swims… and she does a few of these activities daily… and seems to crave the exercise and like it and build it into her day as a reward.

I don't.

And I never will.

She was/is an elite athlete. I'm not.

I wasn't.

I won't be.

So what is normal and pleasurable for her is way out of the norm for me and often not pleasurable. I haven't always done my best nor do I actually know what my best is most of the time. I have been lucky to be able to jump into new, untried territory and come out ahead of the norm. I am accustomed to being successful and winning. Even in grade school and high school I won elections; was voted Queen of the Coronation Ball; was elected Girls' State Governor of Kansas. As a professional adult, I was the supervisor, the director, the vice-president. I have been fortunate. It is not that losing is not in my vocabulary; it has not been my life experience. But this – this training – is all new, and when I master one thing, there is some other new thing to learn. I am not good at this. I do not run fast, and my jumping is still embarrassing. I'm tired and I'm sore.

I'm not sure what the conclusion to all of that is, if indeed there is a conclusion. At this moment on the page it feels a bit like whining. I'm 65, and I can whine if I want to. Now there's a country/western song if I've ever heard one.

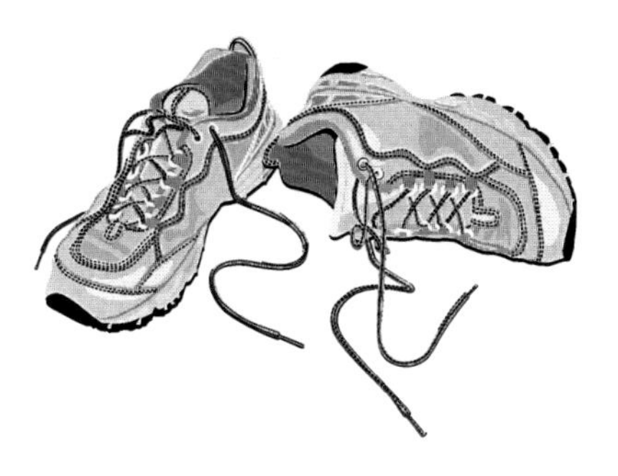

MAY

Gosh, it's May—past the middle—and I haven't written in awhile. I have been busy. I got reallyreallyreally sick for a few days. Some dumb bug or food poisoning. I kept thinking, "What if this was the day before or the day of the Games?" I have this entirely new awareness of how many little or big things could affect an entire career of an athlete. Of course there are many, perhaps thousands, of occupations or professions with random pitfalls to alter a lifetime – ones I have never thought about or even know about. So it isn't as if I now fully get it in terms of athletes. I am simply aware of how my mind never even considered the physical and emotional effort athletes put into training and competing. Years and years. And then one day someone named Tanya appears with a baseball bat, or an ingrown toenail gets infected, or a muscle gets pulled, and suddenly everything is changed. Several years are threatened with a moment of injury. A new appreciation.

I do have an injury right now. Dumb me. I had used some weights on my legs before I was sick and when I started feeling better I started using heavier leg weights. I guess I pulled a muscle in my quads. The only good thing is that after a day of hurting I actually saw in my mind exactly what I had done to make it hurt. This body awareness is new for me. Well, whoopee for awareness. Now I can't run. To be more precise, I hurt when I try to run. I guess there was a time when running through the pain was thought to be the right way. I never would have made it this far with that credo. Surely only ridiculously macho males still abide by that rule. Sooo, I got a massage yesterday, stretched, iced several times… and this morning still could not run. So back to massage today and tomorrow and icing and stretching. This is amazing and a first, as the only thing I ever iced before was lemonade on a hot Kansas day.

I got my registration in for the Rocky Mountain Senior Games. I am signed up for the 100m, 200m and long jump. What I have been emotionally experiencing the last several days is a piece of my personality I have not totally recognized with words before. It goes something like this: I decide, almost on the spur of the moment, to do something, in this instance, train for The Senior Games; I tell people, which is a way for me to feel committed; I garner support, praise, fun exchanges with friends and family; and then BOOM—it gets close to put up time; and I'm not sure I can do it. Yes, certainly I can run 100m, 200m and I can jump into a sand box. But, can I compete in the sense that I am a viable runner and jumper or just some old lady on the track? Now, be clear that I have much respect for any old ladies who will try these things. The reality is that I do not perceive myself as an old lady. So, if I perform as one, I experience a disconnect that is shocking, disappointing, embarrassing, and depressing. Granted, I am a bit of a drama queen; and that's who I am. I am actually afraid of embarrassing any friends who make a special trip to support me. I'm clear, though, that I can't quit; what would Maisy think?

Those thoughts were in play even before I encountered…

The Buffed One

I went to the track, feeling good and strong and agile. I started my warm-ups. And here came a woman who looked like an athlete. She was thin with no apparent extra ounce of anything. Her arms and legs appeared to be total sculpted muscle but not anything weird like the oiled people on TV. She asked if I was training for an event and I rather proudly told her the 100, 200 and long jump for the Senior Games.

"What age division?" she asked.

Again with pride, "65-69."

I then asked her the same questions and I got the same answers!!!

This buffed, muscled, looks-like-an-Olympian person is going to be in my events at the Senior Games.

I don't like her.

I think I hate her.

She seemed nice enough.

Hardly the point.

I think she could literally run circles around me and then handily sprint ahead of me as I lumber down the track. I'm pretty sure that I do hate her.

I wanted to do this. I wanted to win. I thought I could and would. I think I was naïve. I feel embarrassed at my naiveté. I need to work on my attitude. I need to believe that trying is enough. Doing my best is enough. I do fervently embrace the process. I am indeed proud of me for my efforts in training. I could have done more, and I did stretch to do what I have done. The process has been fun, enlightening, demanding, a partnership, a leap toward longevity, etc.

I suppose it is good that that woman appeared. I need to integrate her and probably others into my concept of these events. At this moment, on this day, I don't want another broadening experience that makes me comprehend a myriad of experiences I have never before considered – I just want to flippin' win.

Well, I got that out of my system for the moment. Let's talk clothes.

Bresses Redux

Mary Ann and I went to the Nike outlet for an hour or so and then spent two and a half hours in the Title Nine store in Boulder. Title IX banned sex discrimination in schools whether academic or athletic. I was having my third baby in 1972 when this landmark legislation was passed and certainly did not realize that 30-some years later it would affect my life this way.

Back to shopping. I got a great shirt and some bright yellow shorts which will be my sprinting outfit. The shorts are short too and are real runners' shorts with little built-in panties. I had shorts like that once several years ago. I had never seen the built-in panties and I wore my regular underwear. Well, everything got all bunched up, so I scissored out the built-in underwear. I know better now. I got an additional great top which looks cool with my black spandex Bermuda-length shorts. That outfit would be perfect for jumping into the sand, but, difficult as it is to believe, there are no changing rooms available at the tracks and really not much time between events. What are these people thinking?

Charlie, Ted and Maisy sent me a great Rock Chalk Jayhawk ball hat for Mother's Day. It is soooo cool and is now my regular work-out/training hat. Probably the best part of the shopping in Title Nine was finding sports bras with built-in pockets that my prostheses will fit in. A company called Moving Comfort makes them. The store only had two; I bought them both. There is the comfort to consider with no underwire, no hooks, and soft, wicking fabric. Then there is the look. The outline of a sports bra is distinctive from a regular bra. I wanted that. Silly? Not to me. In the past 31 years, since my first mastectomy, there have been times and things that have renewed and compounded the fear and grief of having breast cancer. I think I know myself well enough to say that, today, I bear few emotional scars from having bi-lateral mastectomies. Of course, I have been incredibly lucky to not have a recurrence. There are, though, still some things which set off my anger/frustration buttons. One used to be shopping for a bathing suit. When I was much younger I wanted a fun, two-piece bathing suit. The special made-for-mastectomy bathing suits in the 70s were frumpy. Each summer I would get antsy, angry, frustrated, and on the verge of tears about bathing suit shopping. Clearly, I saved my feelings about the cancer for that event. One way I got over that was to not need a regular bathing suit very often since I don't swim and no longer live near an ocean. Besides, these days, people wear almost anything they like anywhere they like. Works for me. But, the bra thing has continued to be a challenge, often accompanied by the feelings I just expressed. I want black and navy and yellow and purple bras with matching underwear. In mastectomy catalogues? Not that I found in the 70s. So, finding a sports bra that works without special pockets sewn in was major. I'm giddy about having two of them.

Moving Comfort

I paid a woman $25
to securely sew
pockets
into my bras

she did sew securely
with one pocket upside down

fallen arches are one thing
but a fallen breast
onto the track
as I'm running

that is a leap I do not want

today I am wearing a sports bra
that comes with already made pockets

now that is Moving Comfort

Another Gift?

On the way home from shopping, Mary Ann, in her quiet way, said, "You know, I've been thinking, and I wonder if meeting the Buffed One is a gift. She may be in the lane next to you at The Games, and now that you've seen her and thought about it all, that wouldn't be intimidating for you."

Hmm.

This is May twenty-something

A horrible, horrible day for me. Yes, I know I don't have a terminal diagnosis and no one near and dear has just died, or any of those other things that can make life devastating, and it still is a horrible day.

I got up, ate my pancake and two slices of bacon – the breakfast I'd decided was to be my ritual before the race breakfast. That, plus O.J., has been working for me. I started out for my walk and very quickly had one of my shaky attacks. My arms felt quivery, and my legs felt weak and rubbery, like the one-too-many-runs at the end of a ski day. I felt clammy and wobbly. I turned right around and went home. I grabbed my power drink, gulped some, then ate three Ritz crackers with almond butter and three with grape jam (I don't like p.b. and j. together). I drank half a glass of milk, then more crackers. I found the left-over brisket and ate that, then added some strawberries with extra sugar. I sat for awhile. I started to feel more normal.

I hadn't had one of those spells for awhile. I thought I was being more careful. I take water, sports drinks, and two kinds of power bars with me to the track. When I travel or go on a hike I remember to take a granola or power bar with me. And of course since I had a reaction to mosquito bites I now have to have Deet with me. And the Advil for when my neck starts hurting, as it does every day. And the whatever-the-red-pills-for-gas are. Geez, perhaps I can get a little cart and pull it behind me wherever I go to make sure I have my essentials. Perhaps an extra pair of underwear and a pad or two in case I need to run and start leaking again. Damn, I don't want this.

I don't know much about low sugar (my best medical diagnosis), but what if I had been at the farther away track, by myself? Of course, given how fast this came on I would have been driving there. Then what? It came on so fast. At least I recognized the symptoms as I have had these crashes before. About four in the last year. Well, maybe six or so. But not this quick and strong.

If I hadn't gone through menopause years ago and had a total hysterectomy some years after that I would say my hormones are doing that sad, on the edge of tears thing. I am on the edge of tears. I feel so vulnerable, so old, so falling apart. I hate this. And there is a piece of my mind that knows all the good stuff about my life. Right now that piece is not dominating my feelings. I will feel better in a few hours or a day or so.

Of course, all of this will just get worse as

months and years continue to happen. I so want to grab and hold tight to madness and passion. To joy. To laughter and fun. Now that's a cart I wouldn't mind pulling. It occurs to me that the Games being so close at hand may be making me feel stressed.

That insight came on a very slow train.

More May Musings

This must be another Whine Week. I don't know what happened. I seemed fine. I went to the track, walked once around, did my warm-ups and then decided to jog as one of my drills. I didn't even get two steps in. My right foot acted like it was sprained. I could barely walk on it.

That was a week ago. No running or jumping for more than a week and the Games less than three weeks away. I am a whole bunch of things:

On the edge of panic. What if after all of this I can't compete?

Awestruck once again at the random things that can/do throw a real athlete out of their game

Ticked that I don't know exactly what I should be doing to be the smartest I can be about this foot.

At least my trainer got home. With her advice

and Pat's (massage therapist), I am:

- Drinking more water
- Eating more protein
- Buying some protein powder
- Taking Advil every four hours
- Icing at least 4x/day
- Being careful with my foot
- Trying to notice exactly what hurts where and when
- Scheduling two massage sessions a week
- Going to Bally's to exercise in the water (won't hurt foot)

Did I mention doing my work for classes, for research, for a new project, food shopping, fixing dinner, doing the laundry. Every woman knows that drill. What a dumb foot to pull this stunt on me.

It is odd, though, how out of sync I feel not being able to exercise/run regularly. I used to hate to get up in the morning. I will never spring out of bed; that has to be bad for you. I like to think for awhile and then snuggle into my pillow, perhaps nap a bit more, get up and look at the paper with my cup of coffee. Make a list. Straighten a bit. Think about dinner. More coffee. Think about my breakfast. Shower. Eat. Do my hair and make-up. Then, maybe, out for the day. But no, these days I get up about six, go from my nightgown to a sports bra (!), a wicking shirt, shorts (never thought I'd wear them again, but running in the summer – no other way to go), and my running shoes. No make-up. Ball hat on bad hair. Ready to go to the track by 7:30. Who is this person?

That got to be a routine I was comfortable with and rather proud of.

Day After Whine Day

Massage this afternoon. I went to the chiropractor this morning. (This is beginning to sound like a hospital chart.) I didn't understand most of what he said but he seemed quite clear that something in my ankle was locked and he unlocked it. This man and his magic saved me earlier; I hope it all works again.

I do know that in the world these Senior Games are not meaningful and certainly my participation is even less meaningful, but I have invested my energy, time, and some dreaming. I want to participate. Maybe now I can say, "Forget the medals, forget the winning, just let me be in the race." I guess I am almost at that point. I want to do this.

Meanwhile I am trying to figure out when three different grandchildren (our oldest son Tom's children) can come from Philadelphia to Colorado Springs for their focused time with grandparents. This involves their schedules, our schedules, camp schedules, airline availability, etc. Fortunately, as a woman, I have the skills needed to make it all happen. I feel compelled to note that women as a group seem to multi-task with little effort. Just about any woman can talk on the phone, gesture "No! Absolutely not!" to the child who is trying to juggle the glass animal from Italy, stir the chili, and then add tomato paste to the grocery list on the fridge, all at the same time. Try to get a man to run out of a burning building when he is on the phone. Nope. Only one task at a time. What is that? As Pat K. my 86 year old friend noted, "We're all married to the same man!"

Something really weird has happened to my waist. I have this roll of fat in the front and back. Worse than it's ever been. I mean a serious handful of fat and skin. Everything else is firm and some of it even defined (dare I say "buffed"?) and then there is this roll of fat. Mary Ann's theory remains: it is the last to go and is the extra skin from what I've lost or tightened up. Is she putting me on?

Recently I needed to unlock a high and heavy gate across a road. I didn't warm up or practice or measure my steps to get it just right. I just hopped up, climbed a few rungs, swung my legs over one at a time, went down the other side, and unlocked the gate. Mary Ann drove the car through and when I was back in the car said, "How many of your friends, your age, could do that?" I thought it was kind of a silly question but as seven of my women friends came to mind, I thought that only one would do what I had just done. The others are too heavy or out of shape or too frail with leg or hip injuries. Hmm. I begin to acknowledge that I am in pretty good shape "for my age."

Two weeks before

As I was finishing my track work-out (without running or jumping) I had an Aha. I have two songs on a CD that I play over and over again, usually on my way to and back from the track. One is an instrumental and is one of the pieces played for and at one of the Olympics. It is inspirational and makes me want to move and run and jump and overcome. The other is "One Moment in Time" sung by Whitney Houston. I like it all and especially the line, "Give me one moment in time when I'm more than I thought I could be." I have played that, at a conservative estimate, at least 100 times in the last few months. I sing along. I thought I knew all the words. Today, for the first time ever, I heard a line I'd never heard before: "You're a winner for a lifetime if you seize that one moment in time." Hello! It isn't as if I have not intellectually grasped that, but my gut had not really gotten it. I was hung up not only on not winning (when that finally occurred to me) but on not even doing very well. I was thinking that my friends would be embarrassed for me. I now understand that my friends and family are coming and thinking about me to support my effort, not just to see me win. That looks so simple as I write it, and it is major now that the concept has settled inside of me.

They're playing my song.

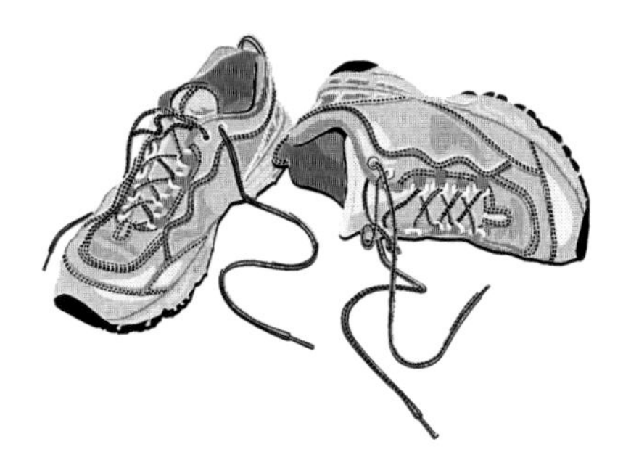

JUNE

Oh My Gawd, It's June!

After my warm-ups at the track I started the drills I can still accomplish without hurting, when who should appear? Would that it were the Santa Guy with eight tiny reindeer; but, no, it was THE BUFFED ONE, again, doing stretches that only a Cirque du Soleil person should be able to accomplish. But, hey, I am in a different space now. Does she intimidate my athlete self? Well, yes. She is good. And fluid. Actually pretty to watch. I even know the details of her good form although her arms are a bit floppy. Then came another woman carrying some curious equipment. Now I get it—practice hurdles. She carried, unfolded, and set up her own hurdles on the track. We talk. Her name is Christel. She is 70 and is going to the Senior Games. Thank goodness she's 70 and in another age bracket. She used to coach track. Just like me. Not. Oh, well, I am who I am and I am going to the Senior Games. So there.

This injury thing – very very tight quad. When I try to run full out, it "grabs" and hurts and I stop. Mary Ann has me practicing in the pool. Me who doesn't swim and barely tolerates the shower. I can "run" in water without hurting my leg. We did this in Cabo San Lucas, so I know how to do it now that I need to – clever, clever trainer person. She has these bar bell like float things that I have in my hands and a spong-y belt thing around my waist that holds me up. We go in the Jacuzzi before and after the pool. I do some of my drills and run in the pool, and nothing hurts. Mary Ann has a great story about a young woman runner in the Olympics who had an injury and could only run in the water in her last weeks of training. I guess it was almost like research in that she did even better in her race than when she was training by running on a track. So we do the pool thing after all the warm-ups that do not hurt my leg, and that makes me feel like I'm still in training.

A couple of days later.

Oh. Oh dear. Oh dear me. Lots of things hurt. Not horrible ouch hurt but stiff old hurts. My whole days now are about my legs. I get up and use the hydrocolators (yes, plural) to heat up my muscles… and take soreness away. While I am sitting with my legs up and wrapped in towels I make a list of what I need to do that day. Most of what is on the list cannot be done by a person sitting with their legs up and wrapped in towels. Most of what is on the list will not get done. Next is eating, although I prefer to have my coffee and wander and gaze for about an hour before I eat. Eating is what I need to do soon so that food can be digested before I go to the track. When I go to the track is time sensitive in that it gets very hot later in the day. Another consideration is that I must not go too early because the temperature should come close to matching the time and temperature of the day of the meet. Then there is the whole bathroom consideration. Halfway through my workout at the track I need a bathroom. There are bathrooms at the tracks, but they are usually locked. I have happily peed in the grass at the edge of several tracks. Other people on the track, however, preclude that solution. I need to say that it is not easy to find a place to train. Every article in the AARP magazines, Prevention, medical school newsletters, etc. say to exercise and to hydrate. Drink lots of water. Well, then what? Of course, I have to pee, and the tracks lock their bathrooms. In addition, what if I wanted to do the pole vault event? I remember Christel, the woman who carried her hurdles with her. I think the only time all of that equipment is up is when the school kids practice or have a meet. All of those publications need to start telling high schools and colleges to invite older people to use their facilities and to make those facilities user friendly. Okay, off my soapbox and back to eating.

I can't just eat. I have to consider the right food groups for the activity that is next. I am not a nutritionist. I am not even someone who paid much attention in Home Ec. That was 7th grade and the first "C" I ever got. Another story. Anyway, I now know that I should have carbohydrates and fats before a race and protein after. I now go about with soft squishy cheese in my work-out bag which has recently added a washcloth and ice cubes in a quart zip lock bag (for cooling me off before I have a heat stroke), deodorant (I actually sweat now and smell bad, the heights of which I always aspired to but had never reached before), a short handled rake to smooth the sand for my jumping, and other items that I cannot catalogue now as that would entail moving.

My writing was just interrupted by a phone call. My trainer. In response to my moans she suggested I take a day off. She said it would really be okay and even desirable. Yesyesyes-yesyesyesyesyesyes. I didn't know I could or should take a day off.

Yipee!

I will keep my appointment with the athletic trainer at ten and the chiropractor at three and of course do my weights and stretches. And ice and heat. Still, a day off. Book Club is at noon. My five friends there have been totally supportive of and interested in my training.

It's getting close now.

Seven months went so fast. I think I should have started earlier. And worked harder. Too late now. Can't believe I have not been able to run or jump for more than two full weeks.

Veet called. She and Rudy are planning to drive the 500 miles from Kansas City to see me compete. I told her not to start out until I was sure that I would be running. I related that phone call to Mary Ann who said, with a perplexed look and tone, "What do you mean?"

"Well," I said, "I don't know if I will be able to run with my leg the way it is."

She looked at me then with steely blue eyes I had not seen the likes of, and with a quiet but measured, low, growl-y, and almost parental tone, said, "Oh, you will be running. It may hurt, but you will be running. Whatever is wrong with your leg might feel worse but you will not have a permanent debilitating injury. You will be running."

Oh.

I didn't know all of that. Shoot, I can hurt. I hurt now. If I know that it won't hurt me in some major way, I can run. Cool.

So I called Veet and told her I was on.

I laugh when I replay that "conversation" with my trainer. She has been so accepting, soft and soothing with me in so many ways, but not then. She was serious. I'm glad. I trust her judgment. One other time was funny too. We were leaving the track after my work-out and going to separate places. Mary Ann said, "Now be sure to eat when you get home, and have some protein. "Well, actually," I said, "I'm not hungry right now."

Again the steely eyes, the growl-y tone, the parental locking of eyes, followed by, "I don't care. Eat."

I did.

How I Imagined It Could Have Been With The Gs

Karen has always been the sexy one, the one with the quarterback and basketball star boyfriends, the one with the Lauren Bacall voice, and legs that go on forever. Her response to my letter about The Games was classic Karen: "Sure! What the hell! I may embarrass you all; but at this stage of life, I don't think about embarrassment much. It sounds like a blast." She goes to a gym a couple of days a week, has had a personal trainer and tennis coach forever; drinks Scotch on the rocks and smokes like a chimney; has a figure to kill for and regularly wins the Senior Division Tennis Trophy at her club. I am so excited; Karen is going to play tennis in the Senior Games!

That same day I got a phone call from Saragene. She is hyper and overflows with wanting to "lose weight, be all together again, and win something!" She is stumped about what event to enter with her "stumpy, short legs." She reports that as soon as she got my letter she started doing jumping jacks and taking vitamins. We'll have to find an event that uses arms!

Judy is cool as usual. She recently married after being widowed for 12 years. She and her new guy live in a golf community. She said she was hesitant about her scores until she looked on the website. "Hey! I can do as well as those old broads." Okay! We've got another player!

What about Veet? She called saying, "You've gotta be kidding. I have never been on any kind of team. I am not an athlete. I've never even thought about any athletic things. Look, I don't want to be the only one not in this, but I can't imagine doing anything. Can I just cheerlead? I can sing... any singing events?" When I said, "You can still swim, can't you?" She said, "I suppose so, but I can't do anything fancy or dive or... what are you saying?"

I think she'll do it.

More Imagine-ings About If the Gs Had

There was little surprise but great celebration when Karen mowed down all the competition, and was the darling of several men, two of whom have her address and have made plans to visit her in Tulsa. Some things never change. And in her sexy gravelly voice, "Linda Glick, I thought you were crazy, but damn this was fun!"

Saragene entered the Horseshoe competition and placed 3rd. She lost 17 pounds in training and says, "I love you guys. I want to do this again!"

Judy twisted her knee and could not

participate. She was our biggest cheerleader and organized water and snacks. Perfect support from a good friend.

And Veet? Well, she never really got into it. Her husband tried so hard to convince her she finally told him if he felt that way then why didn't he do it. Those were not the exact words she used. And he did. Rudy started training to race walk, worked with some weights, and he won his event. Veet could not have been happier. She had done much of the walking with him and lost weight and inches. Veet filmed all of us doing everything. What a gift.

I so wish all of that had been real and not just my day dreaming.

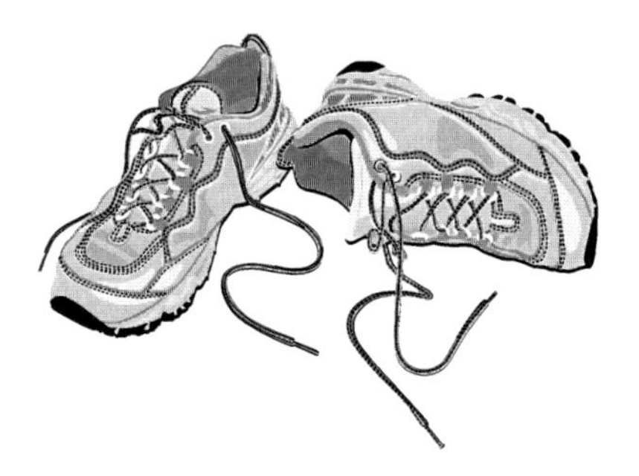

The Big Day has arrived

The morning before I was to compete, I packed my gym bag with its many items. Mary Ann and I drove to Greeley, Colorado, home of the Rocky Mountain Senior Games. Just seeing the banner, "Welcome to the Senior Games" stretched above the street was a thrill for me.

The Bookies and my Cheering Squad:
(upper left, then down) Rudy, Veet, Keith, Laurie, Ellen, and Ken.

Ken and Keith joined us in Greeley that evening for dinner. We met at a restaurant and as we went in, who came out? Yes, The Buffed One. It took a moment for my heart to beat regularly again.

Well, the real Race Day was perfect. Clear skies. Not too hot. I had a cheering section. My Book Club had T-shirts made. They say "See Linda Run. See Linda Jump. Go Linda go!" They drove, leaving early in the morning, and sat on bleachers for hours, and with Veet and Rudy and Mary Ann's and my husbands, made the perfect cheering section.

I had to be there at nine to sign in but my race was not until eleven. My trainer fed and watered me and about 10:30 I started my warm-up. Of course she was there, warming up, all beautifully toned muscle. The Buffed One looked good and strong and experienced. I had not remembered her abdomen. It actually looked like a washboard. Then she started prancing. I kid you not – she pranced. She hopped. She ran in place up/down up/down up/down on her toes, really fast.

The starter called my name first and said, "Lane One." Then he called her name and "Lane Two." Just like Mary Ann said it could happen: The Buffed One right next to me! There were other women in other lanes. I had never started with a gun shot before, but I was ready. The gun went off, and I started. I quit noticing her. It's difficult to explain how I was aware of her without thinking about it or being distracted by her presence. Then I was aware that she was right next to me. She was still right next to me. Then she was no longer next to me. But not in front of me. Then the woman in blue, in another lane, came onto my radar screen. I heard Mary Ann's voice in my head, "Keep up! Keep up! Finish strong." I think I kicked it up a notch and then was over the finish line.

With heart pounding, I realized I was ahead of the Buffed One!

I wasn't sure what had happened. Did I win? I think I won. Nah, I couldn't have won, could I? Time was suspended. I shook the hand of the woman in blue, who I thought had come in just barely after me. Was there a false start? What happened? I was utterly confused. Then over the P.A. I heard, "In the Women's 100 Meter Sprint, Age 65-69, First Place, Linda Glick." I don't know what he said next. Then my cheering section, who reported later that they also felt suspended in time, burst into cheers, came tumbling onto the track and started hugging me. Mary Ann looked slightly more incredulous than I felt and had a smile plastered on her face that just wouldn't quit.

I had won. First Place. By three-tenths of a second. The gold medal.

The Buffed One had pulled back, with an injury I later learned about.

That is what actually happened that day. I got a gold medal for the best time in the 100 meter sprint for females 65-69 and got to stand on the middle, highest box and everything. Just like in the Olympics. I was indeed high on that highest box.

Taking home the Gold. One of my proudest moments.

Odds and Ends

I did get that tattoo.

I also won a gold medal in the long jump in my age division.

I did not run the 200 meter. What was I thinking?

I qualified and went to the National Senior Games in Louisville in 2008. There were hundreds – no, thousands – of women and men my age, and older. Everywhere I went I saw older women and men playing basketball,

Competing in the Senior Games in Louisville with my husband Keith filming.

volleyball, table tennis, shuffleboard; running, race-walking, throwing the discus and shot put; and proudly competing in the many Senior Games events.

This reminded me of the 93 year old woman who won the gold medal in the 100 meter in Colorado. She had to be helped onto the award platform; then she pumped her fist and gave a big grin.

The women in my age division were so nice

The Gs supporting me at the Senior Olympics in Louisville.

Rudy, me, Karen, Veet, Saragene's hair and Judy.

to me. I was once again reminded of how supportive women usually are. I think it was obvious that I was a beginner. One woman who was competing against me took the time to recommend wearing cleats for jumping; another pointed out that I was losing almost a foot by jumping before I reached the line. I recognized one of the women from the *Racing Against the Clock* DVD. There were 30+ competitors in the 100m for 65-69 year old women. I did not get past the first heat. I wasn't jumping very well either. Mary Ann came down onto the track and said, quietly, "See those two women? Don't you let those two beat you."

I didn't; I took eighth place in the long jump in my age division. Eighth place in the National Senior Games! I got a ribbon and got to go on the stage with the other winners.

All of the Gs came to cheer for me, as did my youngest son James, his fiancé Rachel, my husband Keith, Mary Ann's husband Ken, and of course, Mary Ann. I did not win medals, and we all had a wonderful time. Wow.

As I finish my journal, I have eight medals. A couple of them were awarded with no competition on that particular day in that particular event. At one point I was sort of apologizing to son James about "not really winning" because no one else jumped that day.

He said, "Mom, you trained, you showed up, you jumped. You won."

I've always liked that kid.

Mary Ann and I did start a volleyball team. Two of the Gs, Sargene and Veet, came to Colorado from Kansas to train with us. Our members' average age is 70.

We are going to the National Senior Games in Palo Alto in August, 2009. We're still beginners in volleyball, but we are well versed in having fun.

I agree with another member of THE GLAMS volleyball team who said, "I feel better than I ever have—better physically, emotionally, and every other way there is."

See you at the next Senior Games!
Linda and Mary Ann

How to find out more about Senior Games near you.

1. Launch to the internet, type your state and 'Senior Games' (i.e. Illinois Senior Games) into your search engine. That will get you started. The websites are usually fairly easy to maneuver. The website should tell you:
   - when the next games are
   - what different sports are offered
   - where the games are held
   - registration information, etc.

   State Games are held every year. There will also be a list of athletes for each event and their "place" in the event. If you are a beginner, try not to pay too much attention to times, distances, etc. What is interesting is that the participants' names and home towns are noted on the website.

   You can usually find someone who lives near you and chances are good they would enjoy telling you about their experiences and would be happy to answer your questions.

2. Then type in National Senior Games and find out when they are. Nationals are held every two years. Call your local YMCA or local senior center and ask if there are any groups or teams already formed for Senior Games. Many, if not most of the people

who compete in the State Senior Games are not elite athletes; they are people like you, people who want to try something new and fun and healthy. If I can do it, you can do it!

Things To Consider Before You Jump In

This might be the perfect time to have that yearly physical. Tell your medical provider that you are considering starting or increasing your physical activity and ask if she/he thinks that is okay.

Find out what your community has in place for older adults. There are many balance and mobility classes specifically designed for the older body.

If you have not been regularly physically active, start slowly. Hurting is not a healthy part of a good exercise program.

I am including how Mary Ann helped me and the subsequent volleyball team members begin to get into shape.

Mary Ann's explanation of why to do Joint Readiness

Why you should do these
JOINT READNIESS activities:

Doing Joint Readiness (JR) activities increases the circulation of 'synovial fluid' in your joints and prepares your connective tissue, which has a blood supply, for movement.

Synovial fluid provides "lubrication" to your joints.

Connective tissue connects muscles to other muscles (ligaments) and bones to muscles (tendons).

Muscles and connective tissue also have nerves called somatoreceptors) that are "activated" when you do joint readiness. Somatoreceptors are one of the three (3) types of sensory "systems" that are responsible for balance. The vestibular system (your inner ear) and your vision are the other two. When you warm your joints up, these somatoreceptors are better able to provide information about your position in space.

After you have been sitting for a while or before you do more intense activity (like before you go for a walk or do strength-training exercises), it is **HIGHLY recommended** that you do the **JOINT READINESS** activities.

When we sit for long periods of time, our blood is distributed to areas of the body that "demand" it (your gut if you have just eaten; your brain if you are reading or doing crossword puzzles). Your joints "stiffen" when they aren't used. Osteoarthritis further stiffens or constricts your joints. But, doing joint readiness prepares your joints to move… and protects you from injury.

At first, if you haven't been physically active much at all, these JR activities may be a "workout" in and of themselves. Once you get into the "swing-of-it" these activities will be easier to do and almost automatic. You can then add more repetitions of these. For example, you can do them 12-15 times in each direction or 1-2 minutes each exercise.

When you are done, if your joints or muscles still feel "tight," so some "light" stretching. You DO NOT want to work on your flexibility *before* you begin other forms of exercise though. You may "pull" something. Your goal is to WARM-UP; to prepare your muscles and connective tissue for activity. Joint readiness is best for that. If you want to work on range-of-motion around your joints or muscle flexibility, do so *after* exercise when your muscles and connective tissue are much warmer than they are at the beginning.

Do the following series of activities BEFORE ANY other kind of activity.

Remember, if you haven't been physically active for some time, these activities will be enough for a while.

Mary Ann's warm-ups, exercises and stretches to begin

Do the following series of activities BEFORE ANY other kind of activity –

Begin with 5 minutes (maximum) of a general whole body warm-up. If you are at home, this might consist of:

- walking around the house,
- picking things up,
- putting a load of clothes in the washing machine,
- wiping the counter tops off;
- putting the garbage out,
- watering the outside plants,
- sweeping the porch or deck – you get the picture.
- anything that uses large muscle groups.

If you are in a fitness center, you may want to use the stationary bike, rowing machine, treadmill, etc. for 5 minutes.

Then do the following for not more than

30-45 seconds each area (about 8-10 times each direction), warming up each body area. These activities are intended to get your joints ready for 'action.'

Ankle Circles

toes on ground,
rotate ankles in a circle,
first in one direction and then the other

Knee Circles

stand with feet about 5 inches apart
bend knees
place hands on knees
rotate both knees at the same time
in one direction 8-10 times and
then in the other directions

Hip Circles

move as if you had a hula hoop
8-10 times each direction

Trunk Twists

with arms just hanging in a relaxed way,
and feet not quite shoulder-width apart
turn side to side, slowly-- head too
look over your shoulder as you turn

Leg Raises or "Fire Hydrants"

feet not quite shoulder-width apart
bend and lift one leg straight up to hip level
turn it out to the side
touch foot to the floor at "3 o'clock"
lift it and bring it back into mid-line
repeat, alternating legs

NOTE: *Hang-on to something until you get the feeling for this movement; once you get the hang-of-these, let go and this activity will "double-dip" as a balancing-on-one-foot activity!*

Arm Circles

Do swimming strokes –
the front and back "crawl"
strokes, both arms

Wrist Circles

both hands at same time
in one direction and then the other

Now you are ready for more activity! Remember to work on your balance, breathe, have fun.

Some statistics about falling, taken from the CDC website.

More than one third of adults 65 and older fall each year in the United States (Hornbrook et al. 1994; Hausdorff et al. 2001).

Among older adults, falls are the leading cause of injury deaths. They are also the most common cause of nonfatal injuries and hospital admissions for trauma (CDC 2005).

In 2005, 15,800 people 65 and older died from injuries related to unintentional falls; about 1.8 million people 65 and older were treated in emergency departments for nonfatal injuries from falls, and more than 433,000 of these patients were hospitalized (CDC 2005).

The rates of fall-related deaths among older adults rose significantly over the past decade (Stevens 2006).